*Thistle
and Thyme*

By the Same Author

HEATHER AND BROOM
Tales of the Scottish Highlands

THISTLE
AND THYME
Tales and Legends from Scotland

Alger, Leclaire G., 1898-

Sorche Nic Leodhas [pseud.]

Illustrated by Evaline Ness

Holt, Rinehart and Winston
New York

FIRST EDITION

Library of Congress Catalog Card Number: 62-11043

96061-0212
Printed in the United States of America

To Maxine McFarland Digby

Ceud mìle fàilte!

Introduction

SCOTLAND HAS STORIES OF SO MANY DIFFERENT SORTS
that the richness of their variety is almost beyond believing.
Take the legends alone! There are old, old legends which are
as like myths as they are like anything else. Then there are
legends of the supernatural, and of saints, which have come
down to us in old monkish records. And there are the popular
legends, which are sometimes sentimental, but often very
funny, and which were sometimes ballads in the beginning.

Another sort of Scottish story is the cottage tale, which
somebody made up to amuse folks gathering around the fire

on long winter's evenings. There are usually fairy people of some kind in cottage stories. They are true folk tales and have been handed down almost as they were first told.

Then there are the seanachie (shon-a-hee) stories told by the wandering storytellers. They took a bit of a legend here and a bit of a cottage tale there, mixed them together with some of the fairy folk, and perhaps a bit of the supernatural, and came out with something distinctive and all their own.

There are other sorts of Scottish stories, but some of the most interesting are the sgeulachdan (skale-ak-tan). The special thing about a sgeulachdan is that it is almost never written down. The composer of a sgeulachdan was (and still is, I have been reliably told) someone who had won some renown as a storymaker-and-teller among his friends and neighbors. And the sgeulachdan (which translated simply means tale) was almost always told as part of the entertainment at some sort of ceilidh (kay-lee) or gathering, such as a wedding, a wake, a christening, or the like. Sometimes they were told in impromptu rhyme, and almost always they pointed a moral, or had a theme suited to the occasion.

Gaelic folks have never been hard put to find a reason for a ceilidh. Weddings, or the announcement of an intention to wed, are the best and likely to produce the most merriment, but a christening is good, too, and so is the return of one who has been far, and long, away from home. There are many special days in the year that call for celebration, such as the end of sheepshearing or of harvest. Then there are the special seasons and holidays like All Hallows' Eve or New Year's. But no matter what brings folks together, you may be sure that there will be a grand feast spread, and the singing of old songs and ballads, the dancing of reels, and most probably speeches to follow. But in the old days, the high point of the entertainment was the sgeulachdan.

The man who was going to tell it was always well prepared. As soon as he received his bidding or invitation to the ceilidh, he knew that he'd be called upon to tell a tale. Why wouldn't he be, being famous for just that in all the countryside? So he'd be casting around in his mind for things to make it out of, and putting them together. And from maybe an idea he got from an old tale he'd heard, or from something that had happened to someone that he'd been told about, he made up his story. After he'd got it together, he changed it about and polished it and burnished it, until he was satisfied that it couldn't be bettered, and there was his sgeulachdan, ready for telling.

There was a special art in the telling of it, too. When the storymaker-and-teller stood up before the company to tell it at last, he had a way of making it seem to fit the occasion even better. He did this by starting out with an introduction which he invented as he went along, telling what the ceilidh was for, and bringing in the names of the guest or the guests of honor, and hinting at the things he was going to tell about. And when he was well into the sgeulachdan, he'd begin to put in asides about this person or that, who was standing there listening, making the lasses blush and giggle, and the lads shuffle their feet awkwardly and look at each other with a wink or a grin, and setting the rest of the crowd roaring with laughter—until it was their turn to be the butt of the joke. Unless the sgeulachdan was a serious one (like *The Stolen Bairn and the Sìdh*), the telling of it could be a very hilarious affair.

These are the stories in THISTLE AND THYME:

The Laird's Lass and the Gobha's Son: A sgeulachdan from the Highlands on the Inverness side of Beauly. This is a fairly modern wedding or betrothal sgeulachdan, brought here about 1850. It pokes fun at the lass who insists on getting her own way.

St. Cuddy and the Gray Geese: A medieval legend of Lowland origin. In the beginning, it probably was told in rhyme. It may have been a ballad or a broadside. This version was brought from Galashiels, not too far from Mulross (Melrose). St. Cuthbert was prior of Melrose Abbey at one time.

The Stolen Bairn and the Sìdh: A sgeulachdan from Cromarty on Moray Firth. A very old one, and quite evidently one told at a christening, for the theme is the steadfast love of a mother for her child.

The Lass Who Went Out at the Cry of Dawn: A seanachie story from the Lowlands. From Beatock about forty miles or so from Dumfries. This story is unusual because it has practically nothing but action in it and moves along at a fast rollicking swing. Originally, it was probably rhymed.

The Changeling and the Fond Young Mother: A cottage story from New Galloway in the Lowlands, and a true folk tale.

The Bride Who Out Talked the Water Kelpie: A sgeulachdan from Ardfainaig in Perthshire. This is a wedding sgeulachdan. It was told at the wedding of a cousin of my grandfather, who brought it to America and told it to my father, who told it to me.

The Drowned Bells of the Abbey: A legend of the supernatural from Ballachulish near Glencoe. Perhaps told in Latin by the monks, then retold in Gaelic.

The Beekeeper and the Bewitched Hare: A sgeulachdan from Lairg on Loch Shin in the Highlands. It is obviously an All Hallows' Eve tale.

The Fisherlad and the Mermaid's Ring: A sgeulachdan for a wedding from Tobermory on the Island of Mull. The general idea behind this tale is that one's first love is not always one's true love.

Michael Scott and the Demon: A legend from Glenluce on Luce Bay. A Lowland story, as are almost all those in which the devil figures. This is a popular legend, probably once a ballad. Nobody knows how old it is, but it is very old.

It is important to remember, when retelling a sgeulachdan in a book, that these stories were always told in Erse (Scottish Gaelic). The swing and rhythm of the Gaelic must be faithfully reproduced to preserve the cadence, which is almost metrical. Wherever possible, Gaelic phrases and expressions must be translated not freely, but literally, to preserve the atmosphere. As there are no written records of them, a writer can only come by them by hearing them told by someone who heard them himself, or even by being told them at second- or third-hand. Considering this, it is remarkable that the sgeulachdan have come down with so many of the old Gaelic phrases and intonations still intact.

The sgeulachdan in this collection were all told to me long ago, and I have reconstructed them from a few notes and the echoes of their telling in my mind.

Sorche Nic Leodhas

Contents

THISTLE AND THYME

The Laird's Lass
and the Gobha's Son

An old laird had a young daughter once and she was the pawkiest piece in all the world. Her father petted her and her mother cosseted her till the wonder of it was that she wasn't so spoiled that she couldn't be borne. What saved her from it was that she was so sunny and sweet by nature, and she had a naughty merry way about her that won all hearts. The only thing wrong with her was that when she set her heart on something she'd not give up till she got what it was she wanted.

Nobody minded so much while she was a wee thing, but

when she was getting to be a young lady, that's when the trouble began.

She turned out better than anyone would have expected, considering all. You wouldn't have found a bonnier lass if you searched far and wide. But she was as stubborn as ever about having her own way.

Well, now that she was old enough the laird decided it was time to be finding a proper husband for her to wed, so he and her mother began to look about for a suitable lad.

It didn't take long for the lass to find out what they had in mind. She began to do a bit of looking around on her own. She hadn't the shade of a bit of luck at first. All the men who came to the castle were too fat or too thin or too short or too tall or else they were wed already. But she kept on looking just the same.

It was a good thing for her that she did, because one day as she stood at the window of her bedroom she saw the lad she could fancy in the courtyard below.

She called to her maid: "Come quick to the window! Who is the lad down below?"

The maid came and looked. "Och, 'tis only the son of the gobha that keeps the shop in the village. No doubt the laird sent for him about shoeing the new mare," she said. And she went back to her work.

"How does it come that I ne'er saw him before?" asked the lass.

"The gobha's shop is not a place a young lady would be going to at all. Come away from the window now! Your mother would be in a fine fret could she see you acting so bold."

And no doubt she was right, for the lass was hanging over the windowsill in a most unladylike way.

The lass came away as she was told, but she had made up her mind to go down to the village and get another look at the gobha's son.

She liked the jaunty swing to his kilt and she liked the way his yellow hair swept back from his brow and she had a good idea there'd be a lot of other things about him she'd be liking, could she be where she could get a better look at him.

She knew she wouldn't be let go if she asked, so she just went without asking. And to make sure nobody'd know her, she borrowed the dairymaid's Sunday frock and bonnet. She didn't ask for the loan of them either, but just took them away when nobody was around to see.

The gobha's shop was a dark old place but it wasn't so dark that she couldn't see the gobha's son shoeing the laird's new mare.

His coat was off and his arms were bare and he had a great smudge of soot on his cheek, but she liked what she saw of him even better than before.

He was holding the mare's leg between his knees and

fixing the new shoe on its hoof, so she waited till he finished. Then she stepped inside.

"Good day," said she.

"Good day," said he, looking up in surprise. And he gave her a great wide smile that fair turned her heart upside down.

So she gave him one as good in return. "I'm from the castle," said she. "I just stopped in as I passed by to see how you were coming on with the mare."

"I've two shoes on and two to go," said he. "Bide here a bit and I'll ride you up on her back when I'm done."

"Och, nay!" said the laird's daughter. "I just stopped by. They'll be in a taking if I'm late coming home."

Though he begged her to stay, she would not. So off she went.

He was not well pleased to see her go for he'd taken a terrible fancy to her and wanted to know her better. It was only after she was gone that he remembered he'd never asked her name.

When he took the mare back, he tried to find out which of the maids from the castle had been in the village that day. But there were maids galore in the castle and half a dozen or more had been in the village on one errand or another, so he got no satisfaction. He had to go home and hope he'd be seeing her soon again. Whoever she was and wherever she was, she'd taken his heart along with her.

The laird's daughter had come home and put the dairy-maid's frock and bonnet back where she got them. After she made herself tidy, she went to find her father. She found him with her mother in the second-best parlor and she stood before them and said, "You can just stop looking for a husband for me to wed because I've found the one I want myself."

The laird laughed, for he thought it a joke she was making, but he soon found out it was not.

"I'm going to marry the gobha's son!" said she.

The laird flew into a terrible rage. But no matter what he said, it was all of no use. The lass had made up her mind, and he couldn't change it for her. And it was no use bothering the gobha's son about it, because he didn't even know who she was. He'd just tell the laird he'd never laid eyes on his daughter.

Well, the laird could only sputter and swear, and his lady could only sit and cry, and the lass was sent to bed without her supper. But the cook smuggled it up to her on a tray so that did her no harm at all.

The next morning the laird told her that she and her mother were going to Edinbro' in a week's time. And there she'd stay until she was safely wed to her second cousin twice-removed that he'd finally picked to be her husband. The cousin had asked for her hand before, but the laird had been putting him off in case someone better came along. But the way things were, the laird had decided he'd better take the cousin after all, and get his daughter wedded to a husband her mother and he had picked for her themselves.

"I'll go if I must," said the lass. "But you can tell my cousin that I'll not be marrying him. I've made up my mind to wed the gobha's son!"

The gobha's son was having his own troubles.

When the laird and his family came out of the church on the Sabbath morn, they passed by the gobha and his son at the gate. When they'd gone by, the gobha's son pulled at his father's arm.

"Who is the lass with the laird and his lady?" he asked his father.

His father turned and looked. "Och, you ninny!" said he in disgust. "Can you not see 'tis no lass at all? 'Tis a young lady, so it is! That's the laird's own daughter."

The gobha's son had been building cloud-castles about the lass he'd thought was one of the castle maids, and now they all tumbled down. His heart was broken because he was so unlucky as to fall in love with the daughter of the laird.

Well, the days went by till it came to the one before the lass and her mother were to go to Edinbro'. The lass rose from her bed at break of dawn and dressed herself and tiptoed down the stairs. Since this was going to be her last day at home, she wanted to have a little time to be alone for it seemed that either the laird or her mother or else her maid

23

was at her elbow ever since she'd told them she meant to wed the gobha's son.

The cook was in the kitchen as she passed through to the back door of the castle. The cook was picking something up from the floor.

"What have you there?" asked the lass.

" 'Tis a bairn's wee shoe," said the cook. "One of the laird's dogs fetched it in and dropped it on the floor just now as he went through. It must belong to one of the gardener's weans. 'Tis a bonny wee shoe and much too good for the likes of them," she added with a sniff.

"Give it to me," said the lass. "I'll find the bairn that owns it." She took the shoe and dropped it in her pocket.

Around the stables she went and through the kitchen garden to the lane that led to the gardener's house. Halfway there she came upon a wee small old man sitting on the bank at the side of the lane with his head in his hands. He was crying as if his heart would break. He was the smallest manikin ever she'd seen. He was no bigger than a bairn and indeed he looked so like a bairn, sitting there and weeping so sorely, that she sat down beside him and put her arms about him to comfort him. "Do not greet so sore," said she. "Tell me your trouble and if I can I'll mend it."

" 'Tis my shoe!" wept the wee man. "I took it off to take out a stone that got in it, and a great rough dog snatched it from my hand and ran off with it. I cannot walk o'er the

briers and brambles and the cruel sharp stones without my shoe and I'll ne'er get home today."

"Well now!" said the lass, with a laugh. "It seems I can mend your troubles easier than my own. Is this what you're weeping for?" And she put her hand in her pocket and took out the shoe she had taken from the cook.

"Och, aye!" cried the wee man. " 'Tis my bonny wee shoe!" He caught it from her hand and put it on and, springing into the road, he danced for joy. But in a minute he was back, sitting on the bank beside her.

"Turnabout is only fair," said he. "What are your troubles? Happen I can mend them as you did mine."

"Mine are past mending," said the lass. "For they're taking me to Edinbro' in the morn to wed my second cousin twice-removed. But I'll not do it. If I can't marry the gobha's son, I'll marry no man at all. I'll lay down and die before I wed another!"

"Och, aye!" said the wee man thoughtfully. "So you want to marry the gobha's son. Does the gobha's son want to wed you?"

"He would if he knew me better," the lass said.

"I could help you," the manikin told her, "but you might have to put up with a bit of inconvenience. You mightn't like it."

"Then I'll thole it," the lass said. "I'd not be minding anything if it came right for me in the end."

26

"Remember that" said the wee man laughing, "when the right time comes."

Then he gave her two small things that looked like rowan berries, and told her to swallow them before she slept that night.

"You can leave the rest to me," said he with a grin. "You'll not be going to Edinbro' in the morn!"

When the night came, what with packing and getting ready for the next day's journey, all in the castle went to bed early, being tired out. The laird locked the door of his daughter's room lest the lass take it into her head to run away during the night.

Early the next morn, the maid came up with the lass's breakfast tray. Since the door was locked, she had to put the tray down and go fetch the key from the laird's room.

"I'll come with you," the lass's mother said to the maid. So she got the key from under the laird's pillow and unlocked the lass's door. When she opened the door and went in, she screamed and fainted away. The maid behind her looked to see why, and the tray dropped out of her hands. The laird heard the racket and came running. He rushed into the room, and there was his wife on the floor, and the maid, with the tray and the dishes and all at her feet, wringing her hands. He looked at the bed. His daughter wasn't there!

"She's flummoxed us!" said the laird. "Where can she have gone to!"

He and the maid got the laird's wife into a chair and brought her to. The first thing she said was, "Have you looked at the bed?"

"I have!" said the laird grimly. "The pawky piece! She's got away. The bed's empty."

"My love," said his wife weakly. " 'Tis not empty."

The laird went over to the bed and his lady came with him. The bed was not empty, though his daughter was not in it.

In her place, with its head on the pillow and its forelegs on the silken coverlet, lay a wee white dog!

"What is that dog doing in my daughter's bed?" shouted the laird. "Put the beastie out in the hall at once!" And he made to do it himself. But his wife caught his arm.

"I do not think it is a dog," she said. "I very much fear the wee dog is our daughter."

"Havers!" the laird said angrily. "Have you all gone daft?"

But they pointed out to him that the doggie was wearing the blue silk nightgown that her mother's own hands had put on her daughter last night. And hadn't the maid braided her young lady's hair and tied it with a blue satin ribbon? Well then, look at the wee dog's forelock all braided and tied the same. 'Twas plain to see that someone had put a spell on the lass and turned her into a dog.

"Nonsense!" said the laird in a rage. "Are you telling me

I do not know my daughter from a dog?'' And he strode over to the bed. But when he leaned over to pluck the animal from the covers, it looked up at him. The laird looked back in horror, for he saw that the eyes were his daughter's own, and the grin on its face was uncommonly like his lass's own wide naughty smile. And around its neck was the golden chain with the locket he'd given her long ago, that she'd worn since he put it there.

But the laird would not admit it. 'Twas all a trick! So he made them search the room from corner to corner and in every cupboard and press. He looked up the chimney himself and got himself covered with smuts, but all he saw was the blue sky above the chimney pot. She was not in the room. She couldn't have got out the windows. She couldn't have gone through the door, for he'd had the key to it. So it all came to this—the wee dog in the bed was his daughter.

He went over to have another look and as he bent down, the little dog chuckled with his daughter's own pleased chuckle and patted him on the cheek just as his daughter used to do. That settled it.

"Och, you wee rascal!" said the laird, never being able to find it in his heart to be angry with his daughter. "Now what are we to do?" There was one thing that was certain and sure. They'd not be going to Edinbro' that day. So a messenger was sent to the second cousin twice-removed, to tell him that he needn't be expecting them. The servants were told

29

the lass was down in bed with some sort of an illness, and nobody but her maid was to be let come into the room lest they catch it. That was enough to keep them all away.

The laird had his own physician come from Edinbro' though his wife told him 'twould do no good at all. He made the man promise not to tell what he saw, then took him into his daughter's room. The doctor looked and shook his head. Then he looked at the dog again and rubbed his eyes. " 'Tis strange!" he muttered. "I do not see a young lady. I see naught but a wee white dog."

"You see a dog because there is a dog!" shouted the laird.

" 'Tis an optical delusion! Begging your lairdship's pardon, your lairdship's daughter is not a dog," insisted the doctor.

" 'Tis my daughter." the laird roared. "And she is a dog. So be off with you!"

Well, the maid and his wife were right. The doctor was no use at all. He went back to Edinbro' and wrote a learned paper called *"Remarkable Manifestation of Hallucination in A____shire,"* which was read by learned societies all over the world, but didn't help the laird at all.

Then the maid suggested they send for an old wife she'd heard of. The old woman came with herbs and powders, but all she could do was tell them the lass had been bewitched. How to take the spell off, she didn't know at all.

The laird tried a gypsy woman next, but all that got him was the loss of a silver comb she must have slipped into her pocket. It wasn't missed until after she'd gone away.

The laird was fair distracted, her ladyship took to her bed, and the maid went about in tears from morn till night. All the servants in the castle said it must be a mortal illness the young lady had on her and they tippy-toed and grieved as they went about their work.

The maids carried the news to the village, and the gobha's son soon heard all about it. If he thought his heart was broken before, it was twice as bad when he thought the laird's daughter might be about to die. For if she were living, at least he'd have a chance to lay his eyes on her now and again. He felt he couldn't be expected to bear it.

He was hammering away at a bit of metal his father had told him to make a brace of, not even noticing the iron had gone cold, when a shadow fell across the door. He looked up and there was the strangest sight he'd ever seen in his life. A wee bit of a man was there all dressed in green from his neck to his heels, and his shoes and his cap were red. He was mounted on a horse so small it could have stood under the belly of any horse the gobha's son had ever seen before, but it was the right size for the wee man in green.

The gobha's son stared, while the wee man got down from his horse and led it into the shop.

"Gobha," said the wee man. "Can you shoe my horse?"   31

"I'm not the gobha," said the lad. "I'm the gobha's son and I can shoe your horse. 'Twill take me a while, for I've ne'er shod a beast so small before and I've no notion of the size the shoes must be."

" 'Tis no matter," said the wee man. "I've time galore. I'll sit and gab a bit with you till the task is done."

So he made himself comfortable in a corner beyond the forge, and crossing his knees with an easy air, he started to talk to the gobha's son.

It was plain to see that the lad was in no mood for talking. The wee man said the weather had been fine for the time of the year. The lad said only, "Aye. Is it?"

Then the man in green said the fishing was good, he'd heard. To that the lad said happen it was. He wouldn't be knowing.

Then the manikin tried him on the fair in the market town over the hill, but the gobha's son only sighed and said nothing at all.

It was taking a long time, as he said it would, for the horse's hooves were small beyond believing. Shoe after shoe had to be thrown back because they were all too big. But at last he got a set that would fit, and putting the horse where the light fell best, he started to put the horseshoes on its feet.

I'll get you talking yet, my lad, the wee man said to himself.

So, when the gobha's son started to put the shoe on the

wee nag's foot, the manikin said, "Have you e'er seen the bonny daughter of the laird up at the castle?"

The gobha's son jumped as if he'd been stuck with a pin. But all he said was, "Aye."

The wee man waited until the lad finished putting the first shoe on. When he picked up the second leg and started to fix the second shoe to the hoof, the wee man asked, "Has anyone told you that she's mortal ill?"

The gobha's son gave a great big sigh, but all he said was, "Aye."

He finished with that shoe and went around to the other side of the wee horse. When he looked to be well started on the third shoe, the man in green asked, "Have you no been up to the castle to ask about the laird's bonny daughter?"

The gobha's son shot him a glowering look "Nay," said he.

That took care of the chatting between the two until the horse was nearly shod. As he was about to fix the last nail in the last of the shoes, the man in green said, "Would you be knowing what ails the bonny young lady?"

The gobha's son waited until he had finished his work and the horse stood with shoes on all four feet. Then he turned to the wee man and he said, "Nay!" He threw the hammer he'd been using aside and told the wee man, "There's your horse all shod and well shod. Now will you take it and yourself away and leave me in peace?"

The wee man stayed where he was. "Not yet!" said he   33

with a grin. "Why do you not go up to the castle and cure the laird's bonny daughter yourself?"

"Cure her!" shouted the gobha's son. "I'd lay down my life to cure her, the bonny young thing." And he asked the wee man furiously, "How could the likes of me do any good when they've had the gypsy woman with her spells, and the old wife with her herbs and simples, and the best physician come all the way from Edinbro', and not one of them could set her on her feet again?"

"Whisht, lad!" the manikin scolded. "Would you have all the village running to see what the matter can be? To be sure, they couldn't help her. But I know a way you could cure her. If you'd want to."

As soon as the gobha's son heard that, he was at the wee man to tell him, so that he could run to the castle at once and cure the laird's daughter of her illness.

"Answer me this first," the green manikin said. "Would you like to wed the bonny young lady?"

"Are you daft?" groaned the lad. "Who ever heard of a gobha's son wedding the daughter of a laird?"

" 'Tis not what I asked you," said the wee man. "Look, lad! *Would you like to wed her?*"

"Before I'd wed with anyone else, I'd just lay down and die!" cried the gobha's son.

" 'Tis just what the laird's daughter said about yourself," said the wee man with a satisfied grin. "So, since you are both of the same mind, I'll help you!" Then the wee green man told the gobha's son what he and the lass had been up to.

"Och, nay!" said the lad, " 'tis beyond believing."

"It all started because she made up her mind to wed the gobha's son," said the manikin. "So let's you and me be finishing it!"

The wee man gave him two wee things, like rowan berries, as like the ones he'd given the lass as they could be.

"Here's the cure for what ails her," he told the gobha's son.

The lad was all for rushing off to the castle at once, but the wee man held him back.

"Will you be going up to the castle the way you are with your leather apron and soot from the forge all over you?" he scolded. "Och, they'd run you off the place e'er you got the first word in. Tidy yourself first, lad!"

So the lad went and cleaned himself up and got into his Sunday clothes, and a fine figure he was, to be sure. 'Twas no wonder the laird's daughter had set her heart upon him!

"Go with my blessing," said the wee man. "But remember! Don't cure the lass till the laird has given his promise that you can wed her."

"That I'll not!" said the gobha's son. He squared his shoulders, and off he marched to the castle.

35

The wee man got on his wee horse's back and where he rode to, nobody knows.

Things at the castle were in a terrible state. The laird was at his wit's end. The laird's wife and the castle servants had wept till the walls of the castle were damp with the moisture from their tears. The laird's daughter was getting tired of being a dog, and beginning to fear that she'd ne'er be anything else for the rest of her life. She had snapped at the laird's hand that morning because she was cross with him for not letting her wed the gobha's son in the first place. 'Twas a weary day for the old laird.

The gobha's son walked up to the front door and asked to see the laird. He had such a masterful way with him the servants let him in at once. In no time at all there he was, face to face with the laird.

The laird had left his manners off for the time. "Well who are you and what do you want?" he asked with a frown.

"I'm the gobha's son," said the lad. When the laird heard who it was, he jumped from his chair and started for the lad, ready to throw him out with his own two hands. Because it was the gobha's son who was at the bottom of all the trouble.

The gobha's son sidestepped the laird and said quickly, "And I've come to cure your daughter."

Och, now! That made a difference. Where the laird had been all wrath and scowls, he was now all smiles. He caught the lad by the arm and said, "A hundred thousand welcomes! Come, let's be going to her then."

"Nay," said the lad. "I must know first what I'll get for it."

"Do not let that fash you," the laird said eagerly. "Och, I'll give you a whole big bag of gold. Or two if you like. Come. Let's be at it!"

" 'Tis not gold I want," said the lad.

"What is it, then?" the laird asked impatiently.

"Your leave to marry your daughter," said the lad as bold as brass.

"Nay!" thundered the laird. "That you shan't have."

"Then I'll bid you good day," said the gobha's son, and started for the door.

But he never got there. The laird was beside him before he laid his hand on the door knob.

What could the poor old laird do? He had to give in and he knew it. So he did.

"You can have her," said the laird to the gobha's son.

The wee dog jumped from the bed and ran up to the gobha's son the minute he and the laird came into the room. The lad took the berries from his pocket and popped them into her mouth and she swallowed them down. Before you could say, "two two's," there stood the laird's daughter in the wee dog's place!

She took the lad's hand in her own and she turned   37

to the laird and said, "I'm going to wed the gobha's son."

"Wed him then!" said the laird, not too unhappy about it since he'd got his lass back again. "But you'd better go tell your mother and the maids, so they can stop crying if you want the castle dried out by the time of your wedding."

So the pawky lass got her way in the end and married the gobha's son. The laird was not ill pleased for he found his son-in-law as likeable a body as any he'd ever found. So he made him steward of his estates and a good one the lad was, too. So it all ended well and that's all there is to tell about the laird's daughter and the gobha's son.

St. Cuddy
and the Gray Geese

THERE WAS ONCE A GOOD SAINT AT MULROSS AND HIS name was St. Cuddy. If folks who have the notion they know better, tell you it was Cuthbert, don't you be believing them, for the folks of his own place always called him Cuddy and if they don't know, who does? It was this saint who had a great knowledge of birds and their ways and the manners of all wild things in the air or on the land or in the sea. The fame of his knowledge spread far from his own land to others in distant places. Great folks came to him to ask him things they didn't know themselves about the birds and the beasts.

St. Cuddy was a great one for tramping around the country-side and often even by night he'd be stravaging over the hills or along the shore, peeping into this and poking into that and inspecting and examining to find out what the wild creatures were up to.

The birds were what he liked best. 'Twas a marvel what he could do with them. He had such a way with the eider ducks that they're still remarkably tame. Folks still call them Cuddy's ducks. Loving the birds so dearly and knowing them so well, it is no wonder that when he got to Heaven they gave the flying creatures over to him, so he's the saint that's protector of the birds.

It wasn't just the birds St. Cuddy kept an eye on. He looked after people, too. When he was at home in his monastery, there was always a line of poor folks coming up the road to ask for help. Never a one of them went away empty-handed, and the kind word and the bit of good plain advice he gave them did them more good than the bundle of food they carried away, and they went home happier and wiser than they came.

The kind words were for those that deserved them. Whenever he came across anyone that was doing anything he shouldn't be doing, he had a whiplash to his tongue that could give a rare thrashing. And St. Cuddy never held back from using it when he thought it was needed.

Well, being a great traveler, there wasn't much that

went on that didn't come under his eye. What he didn't see for himself, he was bound to hear about, for someone was sure to tell him. So, one way or another he learned about the greedy old wife.

This old wife lived by her lone on her tidy farm, having neither husband nor bairn to keep her company. Her cow was sonsie, her sheep were fat, her henyard was a treat for the eye to see. But she was never one to share what she had. She was so greedy and close-fisted she was a scandal to all who knew her.

She had a crafty way of getting out of giving anything away. When poor folks came begging she'd tell them, "Och, now! 'Tis terribly sorry I am! I'd give you somewhat sure but I've got a sluagh of poor kin and I've got to save whate'er I can spare, for them."

Then, when her poor relations came and asked her for help, she'd say, "Well, now, I'd give and gladly if I could. But more than what I need for myself must go to the poor, for they're worse off than yourself." That way neither the poor nor her poor relations got a thing and she could keep all she had for herself.

When St. Cuddy heard what was going on he didn't like it at all, so off he went to have a talk with the old wife herself.

Now it happened that she had a fine flock of geese that she'd raised. She was mortal proud of them and fed them and tended them well till they were fat enough to drive to market to sell.

It was market day when St. Cuddy came along and met her on the road driving her great gray geese before her. There were twelve of them and every one so big and fine and fat it would make your mouth water to look at them, and think what they'd be like lying roasted on a platter!

St. Cuddy was a very large man, and the way was narrow. He stood in the middle of it and he filled it up so that she couldn't get by on one side or the other.

"Good day to you, old wife," said the saint. " 'Tis a fine lot of geese you've got there!"

"Fine or not," said the old wife, "I'll be troubling you to move over so that I can get by with my geese."

"Och, come now," St. Cuddy said pleasant-like. "The morn's early yet. Hold a bit and the two of us will be having a bit of gab."

The old wife didn't know St. Cuddy at all for she'd never laid eyes on him before. But she wouldn't have cared if she had.

"Get over, old bodach!" she ordered angrily, "and leave me and my geese go by."

But St. Cuddy moved not so much as an inch. On the contrary, he sort of spread himself out further over the road.

"Och, now, be easy," he said in a soothering sort of a voice. "Happen I can do you a good turn, woman."

"The best turn you could do me would be to get on your way," said the old wife. She was as cross now as two crossed sticks.

St. Cuddy could see well that folks had been telling no lies about the old wife, but he was willing to give her a chance.

"They tell me you've been saving a goose for your poor kin over at Mulross," said he. " 'Tis on my way to Mulross I am myself. I'll just be taking it along with me and save you the trouble of the journey."

"A goose for my poor kin indeed!" the old wife cried with scorn. "If my kin were as careful and thrifty as me they'd have a goose of their own."

"Och, well! Maybe so, maybe so," the good saint agreed. "But what of the one that I hear you've been setting by for the poor? We've a wheen of poor folk over at Mulross. How about me taking yon fat one along with me for them? Then you'll have done with that." And he pointed his finger at the best goose of the lot.

The old woman flew into a rage. "Not my kin nor the poor nor anyone else shall ever have one of my geese," she shouted. "As sure as I stand in this place. So be on your way, you blethering old man!" And she raised the stick she was driving the geese with and made as if to rush at the saint to drive him away.

St. Cuddy raised his hand and thundered out in a mighty

voice. "As sure as you stand in this place, old wife? Then stand in this place you shall! And the geese you would not part with, for love of kin or charity to the poor, shall keep you company!"

And true it was. For where she stood she stayed. She and her twelve fat gray geese had all turned into great gray stones.

And if you should be coming along from Mulross toward the sea, you can see them for yourself. Twelve round gray stones in a line and a bigger one behind them just where the road makes a bend to get around them.

When the auld wife didn't come back, the poor relations got her farm. Now that they had a bit of gear of their own, they were as thrifty as anybody needs to be. But they were always good to the poor, for they remembered what it was like when they were poor themselves.

If you are thinking 'twas a hard thing that the gray geese should share the old wife's fate, remember they were all headed for market and if she'd got them there, they'd all soon have been roasted and eaten up. So no doubt the geese were well content with the way things turned out, and St. Cuddy had done the very best thing for them after all.

The Stolen Bairn
and the Sìdh

THERE WAS A PATH THAT RAN ALONG NEAR THE EDGE OF a cliff above the sea, and along this path in the gloaming of a misty day, came two fairy women of the Sìdh. All of a sudden both of them stopped and fixed their eyes on the path before them. There in the middle of the path lay a bundle. Though naught could be seen of what was in it, whatever it was, moved feebly and made sounds of an odd, mewling sort.

The two women of the Sìdh leaned over and pushed away the wrappings of the bundle to see what they had found.

When they laid their eyes upon it, they both stood up and looked at each other.

" 'Tis a bairn," said the first of them.

" 'Tis a mortal bairn," said the other.

Then they looked behind them and there was nothing there but the empty moor with the empty path running through it. They turned about and looked before them and saw no more than they had seen behind them. They looked to the left and there was the rising moor again with nothing there but the heather and gorse running up to the rim of the sky. And on their right was the edge of the cliff with the sea roaring below.

Then the first woman of the Sidh spoke and she said, "What no one comes to be claiming is our own." And the second woman picked up the bairn and happed it close under her shawl. Then the two of them made off along the path faster than they had come and were soon out of sight.

About the same time, two fishermen came sailing in from the sea with their boat skirling along easy and safe away from the rocks. One of them looked up at the face of the black steep cliff and let out a shout.

"What's amiss?" asked the other.

"I'm thinking someone's gone over the cliff!" said the first man. "Do you not see?"

The other one peered through the gloaming. "I see a bit of somewhat," said he. "Happen 'tis a bird."

"No bird is so big," said the first fisherman, and he laid his hand on the tiller of the boat.

"You'll not be going in! The boat'll break up on the rocks!" cried his companion.

"Och, we'll not break up. Could I go home and eat my supper in peace thinking that some poor body might be lying out here and him hurt or dying?" And he took the boat in.

It came in safe, and they drew it above the waves. Up the cliff the two of them climbed and there they found a young lass lying on a shelf of rock. They got her down and laid her in the boat, and off they sailed for home.

When they got there, they gave her over to the women to nurse and tend. They found that she was not so much hurt as dazed and daft. But after two days she found her wits and looked up at them.

"Where is my babe?" she cried then. "Fetch my bairn to me!"

At that, the women drew back and looked at one another, not knowing what to say. For they surely had no bairn to give her!

At last one old cailleach went over to her and said, "Poor lass. Call upon your Creator for strength! There was no bairn with you upon the cliff. Happen he fell from your arms to the sea."

"That he did not!" she cried impatiently. "I wrapped him warm and laid him safe on the path while I went to search for water for him to drink. I did not have him with me when I fell. I must go find him!"

But they would not let her go, for she was still too weak from her fall o'er the cliff. They told her the men would go by the path and fetch the bairn to her. So the men went, and they walked the path from one end to the other, but never a trace of the bairn did they find. They searched the whole of the livelong day, and at night they came back and told her. They tried to comfort her as well as they could. He'd surely been found, they said, by a passer-by, and he'd be safe and sound in some good soul's house. They'd ask around. And so they did. But nobody had seen the child at all.

She bided her time till her strength came back. Then she thanked them kindly for all they'd done and said she'd be going now to find her bairn. He was all she had in the world, for his father was dead.

The fisherfolk would have had her remain with them. They'd long given the child up for dead, and they'd learned to love her well.

"I'll come back and bide with you when I have my bairn again," said she. "But until then, farewell."

She wandered about from croft to croft and from village to village, but no one had seen him nor even so much as heard of anyone finding such a bairn. At last in her wandering she came to a place where some gypsies had made their camp. "Have you seen my bairn?" she asked. For she knew they traveled far and wide and she hoped that they might know where he was. But they could tell her nothing except that all the bairns they had were their own. She was so forlorn and weary that they felt pity for her. They took her in and bathed her tired feet and fed her from their own pot.

When they had heard her story, they said she must bide with them. At the end of the week they'd be journeying north to meet others of their clan. They had an ancient grandmother there who had all the wisdom in the world. Perhaps she'd be able to help.

So she stayed with the gypsies and traveled northward with them. When they got there, they took her to the ancient grandmother and asked her to help the lass.

"Sit thee down beside me," the old crone said, "and let me take thy hand." So the grieving lass sat down beside her and there the two of them stayed, side by side and hand in hand.

The hours went by and night came on and when it was midnight the ancient grandmother took her hand from the lass's hand. She took herbs from the basket which stood at her side and threw them on the fire. The fire leaped up, and the smoke that rose from the burning herbs swirled round the old gypsy's head. She looked and listened as the fire burned hot. When it had died down, she took the lass's hand again and fondled it, weeping sorrowfully the while.

"Give up thy search, poor lass," said she, "for thy bairn

has been stolen away by the Sìdh. They have taken him into the Sìdhean, and what they take there seldom comes out again."

The lass had heard tell of the Sìdh. She knew that there were no other fairies so powerful as they.

"Can you not give me a spell against them," she begged, "to win my bairn back to me?"

The ancient grandmother shook her head sadly. "My wisdom is only as old as man," she said. "But the wisdom of the Sìdh is older than the beginning of the world. No spell of mine could help you against them."

"Ah, then," said the lass, "if I cannot have my bairn back again, I must just lie down and die."

"Nay," said the old gypsy. "A way may yet be found. Wait yet a while. Bide here with my people till the day we part. By that time I may find a way to help you."

When the day came for the gypsies to part and go their separate ways, the old gypsy grandmother sent for the lass again.

"The time has come for the people of the Sìdh to gather together at the Sìdhean," said she. "Soon they will be coming from all their corners of the land to meet together. There they will choose one among them to rule over them for the next hundred years. If you can get into the Sìdhean with them, there is a way that you may win back your bairn for yourself."

"Tell me what I must do!" said the lass eagerly.

"For all their wisdom, the Sìdh have no art to make anything for themselves," said the old gypsy woman. "All that they get they must either beg or steal. They have great vanity and desire always to possess a thing which has no equal. If you can find something that has not its like in all the world you may be able to buy your bairn back with it."

"But how can I find such a thing?" asked the lass. "And how can I get into the Sìdhean?"

"As for the first," the old grandmother said, "I am not able to tell you. As for the second, perhaps you might buy your way into the Sìdhean." Then the old gypsy woman laid her hand on the lass's head and blessed her and laid a spell upon her that she might be safe from earth and air, fire and water, as she went on her way. And having done for her all that she could, she sent her away.

The gypsies departed and scattered on their ways, but the lass stayed behind, poring over in her mind the things that she had been told.

'Twould be not one but two things she must have. One would buy her into the Sìdhean, and the other would buy her bairn out of it. And they must be rich and rare and beyond compare, with no equal in the world, or the Sìdh would set no value upon them. Where could a poor lass like herself find the likes of that?

She couldn't think at all at first because her mind was in

such a maze. But after a while she set herself to remember all the things she'd ever been told of that folks spoke of with wonder. And out of them all, the rarest things that came to her mind were the white cloak of Nechtan and the golden stringed harp of Wrad. And suddenly her mind was clear and she knew what she must do.

Up she got and made her way to the sea. There she went up and down, clambering over the sharp rocks, gathering the soft white down, shed from the breasts of the eider ducks that nested there.

The rocks neither cut nor bruised her hands and feet, nor did the waves beat upon her with the rising tide. The heat of the sun did her no harm, and the gales and tempests held away from her and let her work in peace. True it was, the spell of the ancient gypsy grandmother protected her from earth and water, fire and air.

When she had gathered all the down she needed, she sat herself down and wove a cloak of it so soft and white that one would have thought it a cloud she had caught from the sky.

When the cloak was finished, she cut off her long golden hair. She put a strand of it aside and with the rest she wove a border of golden flowers and fruits and leaves all around the edges of the cloak. Then she laid the cloak under a bit of gorse.

Off she went, hunting up and down the shore, seeking

for something to make the frame of her harp. And she found the bones of some animal of the sea, cast up by the waves. They were bleached by the sun and smoothed by the tides till they looked like fine ivory. She bent them and bound them till she had a frame for the harp. Then she strung it with strings made from the strand of hair she had laid aside. She stretched the strings tight and set them in tune and then she played upon it. And the music of the harp was of such sweetness that the birds lay motionless on the air to listen to it.

She laid the cloak on her shoulders and took the harp on her arm and set off for the Sìdhean. She traveled by high road and byroad, by open way and by secret way, by daylight and by moonlight, until at last she came to the end of her journey.

She hid herself in a thicket at the foot of the Sìdhean. Soon she could see the Sìdh people coming. The lass watched from behind the bushes as they walked by. They were a tall dark people with little in size or feature to show that they belonged to the fairy folk, except that their ears were long and narrow and pointed at the top and their eyes and brows were set slantwise in their faces.

As the lass had hoped, one of the Sìdh came late, after all the rest had passed by into the Sìdhean. The lass spread out the cloak to show it off at its best. She stepped out from the thicket and stood in the way of the fairy. The woman of

the Sìdh stepped back and looked into her face. "You are not one of us!" she cried angrily. "What has a mortal to do at a gathering of the Sìdh?"

And then she saw the cloak. It flowed and rippled from the collar to the hem, and the gold of the border shone as the sea waves shine with the sun upon them. The Sìdh woman fell silent, but her slanting eyes swept greedily over the cloak and grew bright at sight of it.

"What will you take for the cloak, mortal?" she cried. "Give it to me!"

"The cloak is not for sale," said the lass. Cunningly she swirled its folds so the light shimmered and shone upon it, and the golden fruits and flowers glowed as if they had life of their own.

"Lay the cloak on the ground and I'll cover it over with shining gold, and you may have it all if you'll leave me the cloak," the fairy said.

"All the gold of the Sìdh cannot buy the cloak," said the lass. "But it has its price. . ."

"Tell me then!" cried the Sìdh woman, dancing with impatience. "Whate'er its price you shall have it!"

"Take me with you into the Sìdhean and you shall have the cloak," the lass said.

"Give me the cloak!" said the fairy, stretching her hand out eagerly. "I'll take you in."

56   But the lass wouldn't give the cloak up yet. She knew the

Sìdh were a thieving race that will cheat you if ever they can.

"Och, nay!" she said. "First you must take me into the Sìdhean. Then you may take the cloak and welcome."

So the fairy caught her hand and hurried her up the path. As soon as they were well within the Sìdhean the lass gave up the cloak.

When the people of the Sìdh saw that a mortal had come among them, they rushed at her to thrust her out. But the lass stepped quickly behind the fairy who had brought her in. When the fairy people saw the cloak they forgot the lass completely. They all crowded about the one who had it, reaching to touch it and begging to be let try it on.

The lass looked about her and there on a throne at the end of the hall she saw the new king of the Sìdh. The lass walked through the Sìdh unheeded and came up to him boldly, holding the harp up for him to see.

"What have you there, mortal?" asked the king.

" 'Tis a harp," said the lass.

" I have many a harp," said the king, showing but little interest.

"But never a one such as this!" the lass said. And she took the harp upon her arm and plucked the golden strings with her fingers. From the harp there rose upon the air one note filled with such wild love and longing that all the Sìdh turned from the cloak to wonder at it.

57

The king of the Sìdh stretched out both hands. "Give me the harp!" he cried.

"Nay!" said the lass. " 'Tis mine!"

A crafty look came into the king's eyes. But he only said idly, "Och, well, keep it then. But let me try it once to see if the notes are true."

"Och, they're true enough," the lass answered. "I set it in tune with my own hands. It needs no trying." She knew well that if he ever laid his hands upon it, she'd never get it back into her own.

"Och, well," said the king. " 'Tis only a harp after all. Still, I've taken a fancy to it. Name your price and mayhap we'll strike a bargain."

"That I'd not say," said the lass. "I made the harp with my own hands and I strung it with my own golden hair. There's not another its like in the world. I'm not liking to part with it at all."

The king could contain himself no longer. "Ask what you will!" he cried. "Whatever you ask I'll give. But let me have the harp!"

And now she had him!

"Then give me my bairn your women stole from the path along the black cliff by the sea," said the lass.

The king of the Sìdh sat back in his throne. This was a price he did not want to pay. He had a mind to keep the bairn amongst them.

So he had them bring gold and pour it in a great heap at her feet.

"There is a fortune your king himself might envy," he said. "Take all of it and give me the harp."

But she only said, "Give me my bairn."

Then he had them add jewels to the heap till she stood waist-deep in them. "All this shall be yours," he tempted her. " 'Tis a royal price for the harp."

But she stood steadfast and never looked down at the jewels.

"Give me my bairn!" said she.

When he saw that she would not be moved, he had to tell them to fetch the child for her. They brought the bairn and he knew his mother at once and held out his arms to her. But the king held him away from her and would not let her take him.

"The harp first!" said the king.

"The bairn first!" said the lass. And she would not let him lay hand on the harp till she had what she wanted. So the king had to give in. And once she had the child safe in her arms, she gave up the harp.

The king struck a chord upon the harp and then he 59

began to play. The music rose from the golden strings and filled all the Sidhean with music so wonderful that all the people of the Sìdh stood spellbound in their tracks to listen. So rapt were they that when the lass walked out of the Sidhean with her bairn in her arms, they never saw her go. So, she left them there with the king on his throne playing his harp, and all of the people of the Sìdh standing still to listen—maybe for the next hundred years for all anyone knows.

The lass took her bairn back to the fisherfolk who had been kind to her, as she'd promised to do. And she and her bairn dwelt happily there all the rest of their days.

The Lass Who Went Out
at the Cry of Dawn

THERE WAS ONCE A LASS WHO WENT OUT AT THE CRY OF dawn to wash her face in the morning dew to make it bonnier, and she never came home again.

Her father searched for her, and her mother wept for her, but all her father's searching and her mother's greeting didn't fetch the lass back home.

She had a younger sister who loved her dearly, and who said she'd go herself into the wide world and travel about to find her sister and she'd not come home till she found her, for she wasn't content to bide at home without her.

So her father gave the younger sister his blessing to take along with her, and a purse with a piece of gold in it to help her on her way.

Her mother made up a packet of things for her to take along. There was a bobbin of yarn and a golden needle, a paper of pins and a silver thimble, and a wee sharp knife all done up in a fair white towel. And she had her mother's blessing, too.

She wandered up and down the world for many a weary day. Then in her wanderings, some one told her there was a wicked wizard who lived on Mischanter Hill who was known to steal young maids away, and maybe 'twas he who had taken the lass's older sister.

Now that the lass knew where she was going, she wandered no more, but off she made for Mischanter Hill.

When she got there, she saw it 'twould be a terrible hard climb, for the road was steep and rocky all the way. So she sat down on a stone at the foot to rest a bit before she went on.

While she was sitting there, along came a tinker body. He was between the shafts of a cart loaded with pots and kettles and pans, lugging it and tugging it along the stony road. He stopped when he saw the younger sister and gave her a "good day."

"Lawks!" said she to him. " 'Tis a wearisome task to be doing the work of a horse."

" 'Tis that!" the tinker agreed, "but beggars cannot be choosers. I've no money to buy a horse so I must just go on moiling and toiling with my load."

"Well now," said she, "I've a bit of gold my father gave me I've ne'er had need for. 'Tis doing nobody any good while it lies in my pocket. Take it and welcome, and buy yourself a horse."

The tinker took the purse in his hand and looked at her. "I've been pulling that load for a weary long time," said he, "and though I've met many on my way, not one has given me as much as a kind word before. If you are going up the hill to the wizard's castle, I'll give you a few words to take along

with you. What you see and what you hear are not what they seem to be. And my advice to you is that you'd better far go back the way you came, for the wizard who lives at the top of the hill will enchant you if he can. But I doubt you'll heed it."

"That I won't," said the lass. "But thank you kindly, anyway." So the tinker turned his cart about and went back down the road while the lass began to climb the long steep hill.

When she got about halfway up the hill, she came across a poor ragged bodach standing by the road. His clothes were all tatters and patches, and he was pinning the rents together with thorns. As fast as he pinned them, the thorns broke, so he'd have to start all over again.

"Lawks," said the lass. " 'Tis wearisome work trying to mend with thorns. Now, hold a bit, " said she. "I've a paper of pins my mother gave me that I've ne'er had use for. They're no good to anybody while they lie in my bundle. Take them and do your mending with them."

The poor ragged bodach took the pins and he looked at her and said, "I've stood here many a weary day, and many have passed me by, but no one ever gave me so much as a kind word before. I've naught to give in return but a few words for you to take along with you. Gold and silver are a match for evil. If you're going up to the wizard's castle, my advice to you is to turn back and go the way you came, because he's a terribly wicked wizard and he'll lay a spell upon you if he can. But I doubt you'll take it."

"That I won't!" said she. "But thank you kindly, anyway."

So she left the poor bodach there, mending his clothes with the pins, and went on up to the top of the hill.

When she got to the top of the hill, there was the wizard's castle standing across a big courtyard inside a high stone wall. She opened the gates, and went across the courtyard, and knocked boldly on the castle door. The wizard himself opened it to her. The minute she saw him she knew who he was for there was such evil in his face as she'd never seen before. But he spoke to her politely enough and asked her what she'd come for.

"I'd like my older sister," said she, "for I hear you've brought her here."

"Come in," said he, throwing the door wide. "I'll see if I can find her." He took her into a room and left her there, and shut the door behind him.

She looked about the room, but there was no sign of her sister anywhere, so she sat down to wait. All of a sudden she heard flames crackling, and the room was filled with smoke. The flames sprang at her from the walls, and she could feel their heat. "Lawks!" she cried. "The castle's on fire!" And she was about to spring from her chair and run
away from the room when she remembered what the tinker

body had said: What you see and hear are not what they seem to be! Then said she, "Och, no doubt 'tis only some of the wizard's magic arts." So she paid the smoke and the flames no heed, and they went away.

She sat back in the chair and waited again for a while, and then she heard a voice calling and weeping. It was the voice of her sister that she was seeking, and she was calling her by name. The lass jumped from her chair, ready to run and find her sister. Then she remembered the tinker's words again. What you see and hear are not what they seem to be. Said she, "Och, 'tis only the wizard's magic again, to be sure." But the voice went on calling her, and she could scarce keep her feet from running to find where it came from. So she took the bobbin of yarn from her packet and bound her arm to the chair, passing the yarn round and round until it was all used up. Now she was safe, for no matter how she pulled, the yarn held fast. After a while the voice stopped calling, and the sound of the weeping died away and all was still. Then the lass took out the wee knife and cut herself free from the chair.

Just after that, the wizard came back and when he saw her sitting there, waiting, he looked surprised and not too pleased. But he told her to come along with him and maybe they'd find her sister. There were a lot of maidens came from here and there to the castle, he told her. She'd have to pick her sister out for herself.

67

They went along to another room and when she went in she stopped and stared. There was nothing at all in the room but seven white statues. Every one of them was as white as snow from head to foot, and they were as like each other as seven peas, and every one was the image of her sister.

"Pick your sister out," said the wizard with a terribly wicked grin. "You may take her along with you and welcome!" said he. He thought she'd never be able to do it.

The lass walked up and down before the statues. She couldn't for the life of her tell which one she ought to be choosing. So at last she stood still, with her chin in her hand, considering what to do next. Then she remembered the words the ragged bodach had given her in return for the paper of pins. Gold and silver are a match for evil! So she took the silver thimble out of her pocket and slipped it on the finger of the first statue. She'd no sooner done so than the thimble turned black as a coal. That wasn't her sister at all! So she tried it on the rest of the statues one by one, and the thimble stayed black as black could ever be, until it came to the last one in the line. She put the thimble on that one's finger, and the thimble shone out so bright it fair dazzled her eyes. "I'll just take this one!" she told the wizard. As she spoke the statue moved, and there was her sister turned back to flesh and blood, with her own rosy cheeks and golden hair and clear blue eyes.

The younger sister took her older sister's hand and the

two of them went out of the room and down the hall, and through the door of the castle.

When the wizard saw they were getting away from him, he nearly burst with the furious rage he had in him. With his magic arts he called up a great fierce wolf and sent it after them. The two sisters heard it come panting along behind them and they took to their heels. They ran like the wind itself, but the wolf came closer and closer. The older sister wept and said she could run no more. But the ragged bodach's words came into the mind of the younger sister. She cried out, " Gold and silver are a match for evil!"

Quick as a wink she whipped the golden needle out of her packet, and turned to face the wolf. He came snapping and snarling up to her with his jaws wide open, ready to leap at her. She reached out and thrust the needle straightway betwixt his great red eyes. That was the end of the wolf, for he dinged down dead.

The wizard shrieked with rage, and came flying at them himself with his black cloak out spread, bearing him through the air like a pair of wings. All the lass had left was the wee sharp knife, and no words of the tinker body and the old bodach left to tell her what to do. But since the knife was all she had, she'd have to make do with it and hope for the best. She put her hand in the packet to pull it out, and somehow the knife got tangled up with her mother's and father's blessings. So when the wizard got close enough, and she

aimed the knife at him, the blessings carried it straight to his heart and down he fell, black cloak and all!

Whilst they stood there getting their breath, they heard a great rumbling noise. They looked over at the castle, and it was rocking to and fro before their eyes. All of a sudden it turned to dust and settled down in a heap on the ground. Being made of the wizard's magic, it could no longer stand, now that the wizard was dead.

The two sisters had no need to run any more. They walked down the mountain as if they were walking on the clouds of the air, instead of the rocky steep road.

Halfway down they met up with a fine young man all dressed in the best of clothes. "You'll not be remembering me, I doubt," said he to the younger sister. "I'm the ragged bodach you gave your paper of pins to. The wizard laid a spell on me that I'd be mending my clothes with thorns till the end of time. But now the spell is lifted, and I'm a free man once more."

The younger sister would never have known him, had it not been that she saw his clothes were all stuck through with pins.

The three of them walked down the hill together, and what should they find there but a fine young man standing beside a grand shining coach. "You'll not be remembering me," said he. "I'm the tinker body that you gave your purse with the gold piece in it to." She'd ne'er have known him

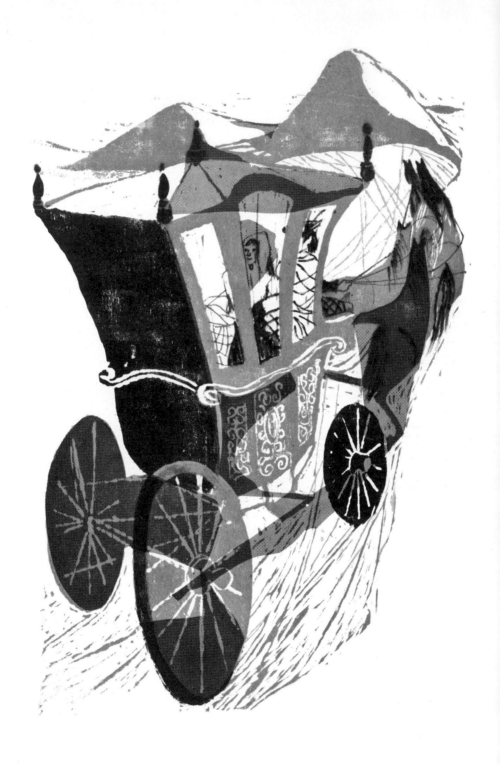

had he not taken the purse from his pocket and given it back. The wizard had laid a spell on him, too, but now that the wizard was dead, the spell was lifted and he was free.

The four of them got into the coach and drove back home. So the younger sister brought her older sister back with her, just as she'd said she would. The older sister married the fine young man with the pins, and the younger sister married the tinker body, and they all settled down together happily all the rest of their days.

The Changeling
and the Fond Young Mother

THERE WAS A FOND YOUNG MOTHER ONCE WHO THOUGHT her babe was the bonniest in all the world. That is nothing uncommon, for every young mother thinks the same.

The trouble was that she would say it, although everyone told her not to because it was terribly unlucky.

" 'Tis what I think," she told them. "So why should I not say it?—there never was such a bonny wee bairn as my wee bairn—so there!"

"You'll regret it," they said. And they shook their heads and told each other, "Just wait and see!"

He really was an uncommonly bonny lad and he thrived amazingly. That is, until the day his mother decided to step out upon the hill and pick whinberries.

She took the bairn upon one arm and the creel to hold the berries on the other, and off she went to the hill.

When she got to the place where the berries grew best, she saw a grand patch of soft green grass in an open space with the bushes all around it. So she spread her shawl there and laid the babe upon it. She knew she'd be fetching few enough berries home if she carried him along while she was doing the picking. His busy wee hands would be getting them out of the basket as fast as she put them in.

The way it is with berrypicking is that one's always seeing a better patch a little way on beyond. She kept getting farther and farther away from the place where she'd left the bairn, without taking heed of it at all. She'd gone a good piece, and had her creel well filled, when all of a sudden she heard the babe give a strange sort of cry.

"Lawks!" she cried. "I ne'er meant to leave him so long!" And she rushed back to him as fast as legs could carry her.

The face of the bairn on the shawl was all creased and red with weeping, so she took him up to soothe him, and patted him and petted him. But he wouldn't leave off wailing, no matter what she tried. So she took him and the creel of berries, and started off for home.

He kicked and screamed all the way home, and he shook his wee fists in the air, and wailed when she laid him in his cradle. Nothing she could do would quiet him and she was fair daft with the fright it gave her.

The only time he'd stop crying was when she fed him. It seemed as though she'd never get him filled up. As soon as she gave him a spoonful of porridge, his mouth was wide open for another. He ate three great bowls of porridge, a bowl of milk and half a dozen scones, and would have eaten more had she given it to him, but she didn't have the dare. She couldn't for the life of her see where a wee thing like himself was putting it all.

From that day the babe never did thrive. He seemed to change before her eyes. His legs and arms were thin as sticks, his breastbone stuck out like that of a plucked fowl, and his head was twice too big for the rest of him. He bawled from morn till night, and all the night through, and he was always hungry no matter how much she gave him to eat. He had the face of a cross old man, all wrinkled and red it was, with the crying that never let off. His mother didn't know what to make of it at all, at all.

When folks heard about the trouble she was having with the bairn, they went to her cottage to see what they could do. But after they'd had a good look at the babe, they shook their heads and made haste to go away again.

When they were well away from the house where she'd

not be hearing them, they gathered together and talked.

"We told her so!" said they.

" 'Tis plain as the nose on your face!" they said.

"We told her she'd be sorry!" said they again.

"All that foolish talk about him being so bonny. 'Twas just beggin' for trouble." And they all nodded wisely. But not one of them would tell her what it was they were thinking. Not one.

Well, the word of the illfaring wean got to the ears of an old cailleach who lived by her lone a little bit beyond the village. She had the name for having all sorts of old wisdom, and some folks said she was a witch. When she heard the tales that were going about, she put on her shawl and shut up her house and went to have a look at the bairn.

"Tch! Tch! Tch!" she said when she got a sight of the bairn. "Well, mistress," said she. " 'Tis no wonder the babe's ill-favored. That's no bairn of your own! 'Tis a changeling that's lying there in that cradle."

When the young mother heard that, she threw her apron over her face and burst into tears.

"I doubt ye've been goin' about telling folks how bonny your bairn was," scolded the old woman.

"Och, I did! I did!" cried the young mother. "Even after they told me not to do so."

"Och, aye. And the fairies heard you say it. They'd not rest after that, till they got hold of your bonny bairn and put one of their ugly brats in his place. When did they switch him on you?"

"It must have been whilst I was gathering whinberries on the hill, for he's never been the same since that day. 'Twas but a wee while I was away from him, but it could have been then they did it." And she fell to weeping almost as loud as the squalling creature in the cradle.

"Hauld your whisht!" the old woman said sharply. "Be quiet, lass! Things are never so bad that they can't be mended, a bit at least. Run and fetch a bundle of grass that your bairn lay on, and give me the shawl you spread for him. We'll have the fairies' babe out of the cradle and your own back in gey soon."

The bairn's mother ran off to the hill, and found the patch of bright green grass circled round with bushes where she'd laid her babe. She gathered a great bundle of it and happed it up in her apron and fetched it back to the old woman. Then the old woman asked for the shawl the bairn had lain upon. The old woman wrapped the bundle of grass in the shawl and set it on her knee and dandled it as if it were a bairn. "Sit ye down by the cradle," she told the young mother, "and neither move nor speak till I give you leave."

Then she got a huge big cauldron and filled it full of water and set it over the fire. And all the time, she nursed the bundle of grass in the shawl. She heaped up the fire until it blazed high and the water began to steam. By and by the

water began to boil in the pot and when it was boiling high and thumping away like a drum, the old woman took the bundle in one arm and a big wooden spoon in the other, and began to stir the water round and round and round. And whilst she stirred, she sang over and over in a croodling tone:

Fire boil the cauldron

Hot, hot, hot!

Dowse the changeling

In the pot!

And all of a sudden she threw shawl, grass and all, into the boiling water!

The minute she did so, the bairn in the cradle sat up with an eldritch screech, and called out at the top o' his lungs. "E-e-e-eeh! Come fetch me quick, mammy, or they'll put me in the cauldron and boil me!

The door burst open with a terrible bang and in rushed a wild-looking fairy woman, with the young mother's bairn under her arm. She snatched the changeling out of the cradle and tossed the woman's child into it. "Take your bairn and I'll take mine!" she screamed, and out the door she flew.

"Well now!" said the old woman as she laid the wooden spoon on the table. "You can take up the bairn, for it's your own. You've got him back safe again." And she put on her own shawl and started out the door.

The bairn's mother picked up her babe and wept for joy. She ran after the old woman to thank her, but all the old cailleach said was, "Have a care after this how you go about so braggart about your weans. 'Tis always unlucky to praise your own. A fairy might be hearing you."

And to be sure, though that fond mother had a half a dozen bairns more and each one bonnier than the one before, she never was known to say a word in praise of them. At least not out loud. Because you never could tell. There might be a fairy hiding somewhere near.

The Bride
Who Out Talked the Water Kelpie

A SOLDIER THERE WAS ONCE, AND HE WAS COMING HOME from the foreign wars with his heart light and free, and his bagpipes under his arm. He was marching along at a good pace, for he had a far way to go, and a longing in his heart to get back to his home again. But as the sun lowered to its setting, he could plainly see that he'd not get there by that day's end so he began to be thinking about a place where he could bide for the night.

The road had come to the top of a hill and he looked down to see what lay at the foot of it. Down at the bottom

82

was a village, and there was a drift of smoke rising from the chimneys where folks were getting their suppers, and lights were beginning to twinkle on here and there in the windows.

"There'll be an inn down there, to be sure," said the soldier, "and they'll have a bite of supper for me and a place for me to sleep."

So down the hill he went at a fast trot with his kilt swinging, and the ribbons on his bagpipes fluttering in the wind of his going.

But when he got near the foot of the hill, he stopped short. There by the road was a cottage and by the door of the cottage was a bench and upon the bench sat a bonny lass with black hair and blue eyes, taking the air in the cool of the evening.

He looked at her and she looked at him, but neither of them said a word, one to the other. Then the soldier went on his way again, but he was thinking he'd ne'er seen a lass he fancied so much.

At the inn they told him that they could find him a place to sleep and he could have his supper too, if he'd not be minding the wait till they got it ready for him. That wouldn't trouble him at all, said he. So he went into the room and laid off his bagpipes and sat down to rest his legs from his day's journey.

While the innkeeper was laying the table, the soldier and he began talking about one thing or another. At last the soldier asked, "Who is the bonny lass with the hair like the wing of a blackbird and eyes like flax flowers who bides in the house at the foot of the hill?"

"Och, aye," said the innkeeper. "That would be the weaver's lass."

"I saw her as I passed by on the road," said the soldier, "and I ne'er saw a lass that suited me so fine."

The innkeeper gave the soldier a queer sort of look, but said naught.

"I'm minded to talk to her father," the soldier said, "and if she could fancy me as I do her, happen we could fix it up to wed."

"Happen you'd better not," said the innkeeper.

"Why not, then?" asked the soldier. "Is she promised to someone already?"

"Nay, 'tis not that," the innkeeper replied quickly. "Only . . . Och, well! You see she's not a lass to be talking o'ermuch."

" 'Tis not a bad thing for a lass to be quiet," the soldier said. "I ne'er could abide a woman with a clackiting tongue."

The innkeeper said no more, so that was the end o' that.

When he'd had his supper, the soldier went out of the house and back up the road till he came to the cottage again. The bonny lass was still sitting on the bench by the door.

"I'll be having a word with your father, my lass," said the soldier. She rose from the bench and opened the door and stood aside to let him go in. When he had gone in, she shut the door and left him standing in the room on one side of the door and herself outside on the other. But not a word did she say the while.

The soldier looked about the room, and saw at the far side a man who was taking a web of cloth from the loom.

"Is it yourself that's the weaver?" asked the soldier.

"Who else would I be?" asked the man, starting to fold the cloth.

"Then I've come to ask about your daughter."

The man laid the cloth by, and came over to the soldier. "What would you be asking then?" he asked.

" 'Tis this," the soldier said, coming to the point at once. "I like the looks of your lass and if you've naught to say against it, I'd like to wed with her."

The weaver looked at the soldier, but said nothing at all.

"You need not fear I could not fend for her," the soldier said. "She'd want for naught. I have a good wee croft waiting for me at home and a flock of sheep and some bits of gear of my own. None so great, of course, but it would do fine for the lass and me, if she'd have me."

"Sit ye down," said the weaver.

So the two of them sat down at either side of the fire.

"I doubt ye'll be at the inn?" the weaver asked.

"Where else would one from a far place stay?" asked the soldier.

"Och, aye. Well, happen the folks at the inn were telling you about my lass?"

"What could they say that I could not see for myself?" the soldier said. "Except that she doesn't talk o'ermuch. They told me that."

"O'ermuch!" exclaimed the weaver. "She doesn't talk at all!"

"Not at all?" the soldier asked.

"Och, I'll tell you about it," said the weaver. "She went out to walk in the gloaming a year or two ago, and since she came home that night, not a word has come from her lips. Nobody can say why, but folks all say she's bewitched."

"Talk or no," said the soldier, "I'll have her if she'll take me." So they asked her and she took him.

Then they were married, and the soldier took the lass away with him to his own croft.

They settled in, she to keep the house and look after the hens and do the cooking and baking and spinning, and he to tend his sheep and keep the place outside up good and proper.

The lass and he were well pleased with each other and all went well for a while. Though she did not talk, she was good at listening and it took a time for the soldier to tell her all about himself. Then she had a light hand with the baking and a quick hand at the spinning, and she kept the house tidy and shining clean. And she had a ready smile that was sweet as a song. The soldier was off and away most of the day, tending his sheep or mending his walls or working about the croft. When he came home to the lass, the smile and the kiss he got from her were as good as words.

But when the year turned toward its end, and the days grew short and the nights long and dark, the sheep were penned in the fold and the soldier was penned in the house because of the winter weather outside. Then 'twas another story. The house was that quiet you'd be thinking you were alone in it. The soldier stopped talking, for the sound of his own voice going on and on all by itself fair gave him the creeps.

She was still his own dear lass and he loved her dearly, but there were times he felt he had to get out of the house and away from all that silence.

So he took to going out at night just to hear the wind blowing and the dead leaves rustling and a branch cracking in the frost or maybe a tyke barking at some croft over the hill. It was noisy outside compared to the way it was in the house.

One night he said to the lass, "The moonlight's bright this night. I'll be going down the road a piece to walk." So after he'd had his tea, he went out of the house and started down the road. He paid little heed to where he was going, and that's how it happened he nearly walked into the horse. The horse stopped with a jingle of harness and then the soldier saw that the horse was hitched to a cart, and the cart was filled with household gear—furniture and the like. There were two people on the seat of the cart, a man and a woman. The man called out to him, "Are we on the road to Auchinloch?"

"Och, nay!" the soldier said. "You're well off your way. If you keep on this way you'll land in Crieff— some forty miles on. And not much else but hills between here and there."

"Och, me!" said the woman. "We'll have to go back."

"Poor lass," the man said tenderly, "and you so weary already."

"I'm no wearier than yourself," the woman replied. " 'Twas you I was thinking of."

Suddenly the soldier said, "You're far out of your way and you'll never get there this night. Why do you not bide the night with us and start out fresh in the morn? Your horse will have a rest and so will you, and you'll travel faster by light of day, and you'll not be so much out in the end."

But it was not so much for them, he asked it, as for himself, just to be hearing other voices than his own in the house.

They saw he really meant it, so they were soon persuaded. It wasn't long till he had them in his house, and their horse with a feed of oats in his barn. They were friendly, likeable folks, and it was easy to get them talking, which was just what the soldier wanted. They were flitting because their old uncle had left them his croft, and they wouldn't have come at such an unseasonable time, if they hadn't wanted to settle in before the lambing began. Besides, they'd never had a place of their own, and they couldn't wait to get there. So they talked and the soldier talked, and the lass sat and smiled. But if they noticed she had naught to say, neither of them mentioned it.

The next morning they got ready to leave, and the soldier came out to the gate to tell them how to go. After he'd told them, the woman leaned over and said, "What's amiss with your wife? Does she not talk at all?"

"Nay," said the soldier. "She's spoken not a single word for two years past."

"Och, me!" the woman said. "She's not deaf, is she?"

"That she's not!" the soldier told her. "She hears all one says. The folks where she comes from say that she's bewitched."

"I thought it might be that," the woman said. "Well, I'll tell you what to do. Back where we dwelt there's a woman that has the second sight and she's wonderful for curing folks of things. She cured my own sister after the doctors gave her up. It was ten years ago and my sister's living yet. You take your wife over there and see what she can do." She told the soldier where to find the old body, and as they drove away, she said, "You needn't be afraid of her for she's as good as gold. She'll never take anything for helping anybody, and if

89

she's a witch, nobody ever laid it against her. She's just a good old body that has the second sight.''

The soldier went into the house and told his lass to get herself ready, for they were going visiting. He did not tell her why, in case it all came to naught, for he couldn't bear to have her disappointed if the old body couldn't help her at all.

He hitched his own wee horse to his cart, and he and the lass drove off to the place where the folks that were going to Auchinloch had dwelt.

They found the old body without any trouble right where the woman said she'd be. She was little and round and rosy and as merry and kind as she could be. The only thing strange about her was her eyes, for they were the sort that made you feel that nothing in the world could ever be unseen if she took the trouble to look at it, no matter where it was hidden.

When she heard the soldier's story, she said at once that she'd be glad to help them if she could. Folks were probably right when they said the lass was bewitched, but what she'd have to find out was how it had happened. That might take time because the lass couldn't help her, since she couldn't talk.

Then the old woman told the soldier to take himself off for a walk and leave the lass with her and not to come back too soon for if he did, she'd just send him away again.

The soldier walked around and around, and at last he found the village that belonged to the place. There was a blacksmith shop and an old stone church and a post office and a pastry shop and a little shop with jars of sweeties in the windows, that sold everything the other shops didn't have. When he'd seen them all, he went and sat in the only other place there was, which was the tavern, and the time went very slow. But at last he thought it must be late enough for him to go back and fetch his lass. Maybe he'd been foolish to bring her to the old body after all. He'd not go back if the old woman sent him away again. He'd just pack up his lass in the cart and take her home and keep her the way she was. If he'd known what was going to happen, maybe that's what he'd have done.

They were waiting for him when he got back to the little old woman's cottage, and the old body told him at once she'd found where the trouble lay.

" 'Tis plain enough," said she. "Your wife has offended the water kelpie. When she went to walk in the gloaming, she drank from the well where the water kelpie bides. And as she leaned over to drink, one of the combs from her hair dropped into the water and she never missed it. The comb fouled the water, and the kelpie can bide in the well no more till she takes it out again. So angry he was, that while she drank of it, he laid a spell on the water that took her speech away."

91

"But what shall we do now?" asked the soldier.

"All you need to do," said the old woman, "is take your lass back to the well and have her take the comb from the water."

"And she'll talk then?" the soldier asked.

"Och, aye! She'll talk. But watch out for the water kelpie, lest he do her more harm for he's a queer creature always full of wicked mischief and nobody knows what he may do."

The lass and the soldier were so full of joy that they hardly knew how to contain it. The soldier wanted to pay the old woman for what she'd done, but she said it was nothing at all, and in any case she never took pay for doing a kindly service. So the soldier thanked her kindly, and he and his lass went home.

When they had found somebody to look after the croft, they started off to take the spell off the lass's tongue. When they got to the place, the soldier and the lass went out to find the well in the woods. The lass bared her arm and reached down into the water and felt around till she found the comb. She put it back in her hair, and as soon as she did, she found she could talk again.

The first thing she said was, "Och, my love, I can talk to you now!" And the second thing she said was, "Och, I have so much to say!"

They went back to the weaver's house, and when he found that his daughter could talk, he was that pleased. He ran

about the village telling everybody, "My lass has found her tongue again!" 'Twas a rare grand day for the weaver. And of course for the soldier, too.

The weaver and the soldier couldn't hear enough of her chatter. They took to following her about just to listen to her as if it were music they were hearing.

After a day or two, she began to grow restless, for she wanted to go home to their own wee croft. So off they set, and she chattered to him every mile of the way. The sound of her voice was the sweetest sound he'd ever heard.

So they came home. It was still winter, and the sheep were still penned in the fold and the soldier in the house, but there wasn't a bit of silence in the cottage. There was this that she had to tell him, and something else she must say. The soldier could hardly slip a word in edgewise, but he still thought it was wonderful to hear her.

After a month or two had gone by and the winter was wearing off toward spring, he began to notice something he had not noticed before. And that was that his bonny wee wife talked away from morn to night, and he wasn't too sure that she did not talk in her sleep. He found he had in his house what he'd told the innkeeper he never could abide—a lass with a clackiting tongue.

He would not have had her silent again; ne'er the less, a little quiet now and then would not have come amiss. But he still loved her dearly, and she was his own dear lass.

So one fine morn after the lambing was over and the sheep were out on the hillside with their dams, he went off to see the old woman who had the second sight to find out if she could do aught about it.

"Deary me!" said she. "I misdoubted the kelpie would find a way to turn things against you."

"That he did!" said the soldier, "or I'd not be here."

"Did she drink of the water again?" the old body asked.

"She did not," said the soldier. "Not even a drop."

" 'Twas not that way he got at her then," said the old woman. "Well, tell me what she did do then?"

"She took the comb from the water and she stuck it in her hair," the soldier told her, "and that's all she did do."

"Did she wipe it off first?" the old body asked anxiously.

"Nay. She did not," said the soldier.

"I see it plain," the old body said. "The water that was on the comb was bewitched again. Och, there's not a fairy in the land so full of malice as the water kelpie."

So the old woman sat and thought and thought, and the soldier waited and waited. At last the old woman said, "A little is good, but too much is more than enough. We'll give the kelpie a taste of his own medicine. Take your lass back to the well. Set her beside it and bid her to talk down the well to the kelpie the livelong day. The kelpie must answer whoever speaks to him, so the one of them that tires first will be the loser."

" 'Twill not be my lass," said the soldier. "I'll back her to win the day."

So he took his wife back to the well and sat her down beside it, and bade her call the kelpie and talk to him until he came back for her.

So she leaned over the well as he told her to and called to the kelpie. "Kelpie! Kelpie! I'm here!" cried she.

"I'm here!" answered the kelpie from the bottom of the well.

"We'll talk the whole of the day," the lass said happily into the well.

"The whole of the day," the kelpie agreed.

"I've such a lot to tell you," the lass went on.

"A lot to tell you," the kelpie said in return.

The soldier went away, leaving the lass by the well talking so fast that her words tripped over themselves, with the kelpie answering her back all the time.

He came back when the sun had set and the gloaming lay over the wood, to find the lass still sitting there, bending over the well. She was still talking, but very slow, and he could hardly hear the kelpie answer at all.

Well, now that the day was safely over, the soldier laid his hand on her shoulder. "Come away, lass," said he. She looked at him so weary-like that his heart turned over with pity. He'd just take her the way she was from now on, silent or clackiting, he told himself.

She looked up and smiled at him, and then she called down the well. "I bid you good day, kelpie. 'Tis time for me to go home."

There wasn't a sound from the well for a moment. Then in a great loud angry voice the kelpie shouted, "GO HOME!"

So the soldier gave his arm to the lass, and they started to walk back through the woods to her father's house. She said only two things on the way home.

The first thing she said was, "I'm awful thirsty," but she drank no water from the well. The soldier made sure of that!

And the second thing she said was, "I'm tired of talking."

Well, from that time on, she neither talked too little or too much but just enough. The soldier was content, for she was his own dear lass, and he loved her dearly.

Since the old body with the second sight would never let them pay her for the good she'd done them, they invited her to be godmother when their first bairn was born. That pleased her more than if they'd given her a sack of gold. But never again in all her days did the wife go out alone in the gloaming or drink from a fairy well.

The Drowned Bells
of the Abbey

In the far-off days when the Picts and the Scots were dividing the ancient land of Scotland and fighting amongst themselves to decide who could get hold of the most of it, there came good men from over the seas to settle in the land.

They found places for themselves here and there along the coasts by the sea and lived wherever they could find shelter and fed themselves on whatever the earth and the sea were willing to give them. 'Twas a hard life, but they made no complaint, for all they did was done for the glory of God.

These men called themselves monks, and what they had come for was to spread the word of God among these strange wild people, who had never heard tell of it before. The monks were learned men and wise in the arts of knowledge and healing. They taught the people and helped them in illness and in trouble. Soon they were greatly loved because of the goodness there was in them.

There was a band of these good monks who settled in a wild deserted place at the head of a deep glen near the sea in the north of Scotland. At first there was only a half dozen of them with a leader they called their abbot. The monks made their homes in the caves along the sides of the glen.

The people of the land at the time were wild and savage and given to the worship of demons, but the monks brought them to gentler ways and taught them to live as people lived in the lands from which they had come.

As time went by, more monks came to joint the band, and the people for love of them built them an abbey so that they no longer needed to dwell in caves.

For love, too, in time the people had a peal of bells made for the chapel of the abbey. There were five bells from the smallest silver-tongued one to the great bell which sent praise to God in deep brazen tones.

The bells were cast in the churchyard of the abbey and made of the finest metal that could be had, by the most skillful smiths that could be found.

Now, in those days there were pirates sailing up and down the sea along the coasts, robbing and plundering wherever they could find prey. What they liked best to find was an abbey, for some of the abbeys had great wealth because of the gifts made to them of money and golden vessels and jewelled cups and the like.

The abbey of the glen was one of the richest, for it had prospered greatly in the long years that had passed since the first monks came. Men of wealth and great standing had sent their sons to be schooled there and had paid generouly for the service, and many were the priceless gifts that had been given to the abbey.

The monks of all abbeys lived in terror of the pirates, and those of the abbey of the glen feared them no less than the rest. Still, the abbey was well hidden and hardly to be seen from the sea, for the stones with which it had been built were the same color as the gray rocks of the glen. Besides that, great trees grew between the abbey and the sea, and screened it with their wide-spreading branches.

The wicked pirates might never have found the abbey at all, had it not been for one young lay brother.

The young lay brother loved the sweet-singing bells so dearly that he would have sent their voices to Heaven in praise every hour of day and night. But when it was known that the pirates were nearby, it was forbidden that anyone ring the bells lest the pirates hear and come down upon the abbey to raid it. It was always the pirates' way to seek for an abbey by day, and when they had found where it was, they would steal on it by night and take it by surprise.

As happens very often, temptation was too great for the young lay brother. For a while he fought against it and only laid his hand lovingly but lightly on the bell ropes when he passed by during the forbidden times. But one evening as he was on his way to vespers, he not only laid his hand upon the ropes but, thinking a very little peal would be scarcely heard, he gently pulled the rope of the smallest bell.

Clear and silvery, one chiming note rang out, down to the shore and across the waters of the sea. But hidden from the abbey around a point of rock a pirate ship lay moored, to take on fresh water. The silver note came to the ears of the captain of the pirate ship, who knew at once that the sound of a bell meant there was an abbey somewhere near.

As soon as they had finished storing the water in the ship, the captain sent out a spy to find where the abbey lay. Then they waited in hiding, until the moon rose and lit the way, and soon after, the pirates were battering at the gates of the abbey.

The abbot knew by the fury of the attack that pirates were upon them. He ordered the monks and their pupils to carry away the chests of the abbey treasures, and flee by a small door at the side to the caves of the glen where the pirates would not think to seek for them. He stayed back himself to gather the cross and the vessels from the altar. A brave man was that abbot, for he had no more than reached the little side door with the rood and the holy vessels gathered into the skirts of his robe when the pirates broke down the gates and rushed into the abbey grounds. He heard their shouts of rage when they found the abbey deserted and the treasure not to be found. He heard their cries of disappointment at finding so little plunder, and then he heard them shout that they would have the bells since there was naught else worth the taking.

When the abbot heard they were going to take the bells that the people had cast and given the abbey for love, he forgot his own danger. He turned at the door and, holding high the cross he had saved from the altar, he called the wrath of God down upon them all.

"Have the bells!" he cried at the end. "Take them if you will! But they will give you neither profit nor good."

The pirates neither saw the abbot nor heard a word of his curse. Up in the bell tower they were, tearing loose the bells and hauling them down the ladder from the bell loft with great clamor and noise.

So the abbot went away from the abbey and made his way up the glen in safety.

When the pirates had the bells all down, they rejoiced to have such a great pile of metal of a quality so fine and pure. They were sure of getting a good price for it when they got

it to the foreign ports where they'd offer the bells for sale. They carried them off to their ship, but before they left they set fire to the abbey.

When they were back on their ship again, they stored the bells in the hold and then they prepared to set sail. The captain of the pirates looked back at the burning abbey and at the sky, red with dancing flames that seemed to reach clear to the moon. He roared with laughter and vowed that he'd never set a grander bonfire nor found loot more to his liking.

But while he stood there looking and laughing, the stolen bells in the hold began to peal. First rang the silver-tongued smallest bell. Then, one by one the others joined in, and last of all the great bell boomed out its deep-toned song. And the peal they pealed was the death knell!

Then the pirate crew came running to the captain. Near-deafened they were by the sound of the bells. They screamed out to the captain that something was amiss with the ship, for the sails were all set and the wind was stiff and the seas running free, but the sails would not fill and the ship would not move at all. The bells were accursed, they shouted.

So then they ran to open the hold and throw the bells into the sea. But before the crew could lay hand upon the hatches, they flew open. There lay the bells rolling gently from side to side and tolling as they rolled. Before the terrified pirates' eyes the bells began to increase in size, growing bigger and bigger and bigger. The timbers of the ship creaked and strained, but the bells kept on growing until at last the ship could contain them no longer. With a great wild noise of crashing masts and breaking beams, the ship flew apart, and down to the bottom of the sea went pirates, bells, and all.

The monks who had been drawn from their caves at the sound of their bells, watched in wonder. They could see the ship by the light of the flames and the moon. When the ship went down, they grieved at the fate of the bells they loved so well. But they said to each other that the hand of God is ever heavy upon evildoers.

Now when the people of the countryside saw the flames in the sky, they rushed to the abbey, fearing that all the monks were dead. Great was the joy of the people when they found their monks safe and unharmed. In thanksgiving for their safety, they built the monks a new chapel and abbey and had a new peal of bells cast, as fine as the lost ones.

There were five of them, just as there had been before, and all were the same as before, from the silver-tongued smallest bell to the brazen-toned largest bell of all. And it is a strange queer thing that whenever the new bells were pealed and sent their noble tones over the waters of the sea, there came back from the sea an answering peal. There are those who will tell you 'tis only some odd sort of echo, but the truth of it is that it is the drowned bells the pirates stole, ringing back from the bottom of the sea. Even to this day you can hear them if you listen.

The Beekeeper
and the Bewitched Hare

THERE WAS A LAD ONCE WHO LIVED IN A COTTAGE ACROSS
the moor. He was a beekeeper, and made his living selling the
honey that his bees gathered from wild flowers and heather on
the moor. He lived alone, and maybe he would have been
lonely if it had not been for his bees. He knew them so well,
and they trusted him so completely, that he could go among
them as he pleased. There were folks who said he even knew
their language and what they said with their buzzing, but he
said it was only the tone of it that gave him a notion of what
they meant. However it was, they buzzed to him and he

talked to them, and whether they understood each other or not, they were all happy together.

One evening as he stood on his doorstep in the gloaming, he heard the sound of hounds baying across the moor, and soon a hare came flying out of the heather with two dogs chasing close after.

When the hare saw him standing there, it leaped into its arms for safety's sake. The lad slipped it inside his shirt and, catching up a stick, he soon drove the dogs yelping away.

When he was sure the hounds were gone, he took the hare out to stroke it and soothe it before he let it go. It made no effort to get away from him and lay quietly in his arms, only trembling a bit from the fright it had got. When it seemed to be over its fricht, he set it down and turned to go into the house to get his supper.

He thought the hare would run away into the thicket behind the house, but it followed him into the room. As he moved about getting his meal, it hopped after him. When he sat down to the table and began to eat, it leaped to the table and sat up prettily beside his plate.

"Och!" he laughed. "So you've come to supper, have you?" and he fed it bits from his plate. Having it close, he took a look at it and saw what he'd not noticed before. The hare's eyes were as blue as the summer skies over the moor.

"I've seen many a black-eyed hare," said the lad, "and I've seen pink-eyed hares with white coats in the animal- 107 fanciers' shops, but never before have I seen a blue-eyed hare!''

It was such an odd creature that it pleased him. And since it seemed to be contented to bide with him, he decided to keep it for a pet. It was that clever and knowing. He'd ne'er seen its like before.

The next morning he took the hare out to show it to the bees. Every beekeeper knows that bees like to be told what's going on in the place where they live, and will not stay there happily unless they are. If the hare was to bide with him, the bees must know about it.

So the beekeeper carried the creature from hive to hive. ''This is my hare,'' he told the bees, ''that's going to live in my house with me. So make yourselves acquainted.''

The bees flew about the hare as if they were looking it over, buzzing noisily to each other the while. The hare showed no fear of them and sat quietly till they seemed satisfied and flew off again on their business of honey gathering. After that, the hare followed him about at his work and took no more harm from the bees than he did himself.

One day as he was working among the hives with the hare at his side, he saw an old woman coming along the track over the moor. He thought maybe she'd be coming to buy a comb of honey, so he stood and waited for her.

But when she came up to him, she said naught at all about honey. ''That's a fine-looking hare you've got,'' she said, looking down at it.

"Aye," said he shortly. She was a stranger to him and he did not like the looks of her. She had a sly air about her that struck him unpleasantly.

"What will you take for her?" she asked.

"I'm not offering her for sale," said he.

"I'll give you a bonnie piece of gold for her," coaxed the old woman.

"I'm not selling her!" the beekeeper said roughly.

The old woman made as if to reach down and take up the hare. As she did so, a bee that had been hovering above the hare's head gave a shrill warning buzz. In a trice, out from the hives and in from the moor swept a great swarm of bees. They set themselves close together, buzzing angrily, and put themselves between the old woman and the hare. The old woman took a few steps back in fright, and the bees flew at her, driving her back to the moor. She ran faster than you'd think one so old could run and as she ran she called back over her shoulder, "Look well to yourself and your hare, beekeeper!" But the bees drove her on until she was out of the lad's sight.

Not long after, he was in the town across the moor with some honey he had brought in to sell, for it was market day. As he stopped to pass the time of day with a man he knew, an old woman walked by. As she passed close to him he saw that it was the old body his bees had driven across the moor. When she was gone he said to the man, "Who was that old besom just now?"

The man made a forked sign with his fingers and looked terribly frighted. "Eist!" he said. "Do not let her be hearing you!" Then he whispered, "They do be saying she's a witch and has the evil eye!"

Well, maybe she was and maybe she wasn't. The bee-keeper wouldn't know about that. But in any case he was going to do what she told him to do as she ran away over the moor. He'd be sure to look well to himself and his hare. He'd grown that fond of it that he'd have grieved sorely had anything harmed it. He knew the bees would watch over it by day, but he took to barring the doors and the windows at night. And he kept a wary eye out for strangers coming by.

Summer went by and autumn came. The first frosts lay on the ground at morn. There were berries on the brambles for the picking. And now the bees were seeking their hives for the winter and seldom did one see more than a stray one or two, for there was no more honey to be gathered from the hedgerows or the moor.

The singing birds had flown south and, like the birds, the gypsy caravans were flitting southward too. Few of the vans came over the moor, for although it was much shorter than the road through the towns, it was barely more than a rough track, and there were few trees to offer shelter or wood for kindling. So when the beekeeper saw a van coming across the moor one chill October day, it surprised him. He came out to the doorstep as it passed by in the road beyond his gate.

Being a friendly, civil soul, the beekeeper raised a hand in greeting to the young gypsy man who sat on the seat of the van, driving the horse. The driver saluted with his whip as they passed by and the lad watched him out of sight. The beekeeper went on with his morning's work, and it wasn't till after he'd had his dinner at noon that he had reason to come to the door again. When he did, he saw that something was lying in the road just past the gate. He walked down to look at it and found that it was a sack of grain. He knew at once that it had dropped from the gypsy van. They'd lost it from under the wagon bed where they usually carried such things.

"Och, they'll never miss it before they make camp for the night," he said. He was troubled in his mind because he knew that it would be too late and too dark for them to come back for it then. He did not like to think of the poor gypsy horse going without its evening meal. So as he could well spare the time, he got out his market cart and hitched his own wee nag to it, and took off after the gypsy van with the sack of grain.

His horse was used to the road, and his cart much lighter than their loaded van, so in an hour or so he caught up with them. He hailed them and when they stopped, he pulled up alongside of the van. He handed the gypsy driver the sack of grain. "You dropped this in the road by my place," he said. "I brought it along because I thought you might be needing it bad tonight."

The gypsy took the sack with a look of surprise.

"I take it kindly," said he. "You mean to say you fetched it all the way from the house back yonder by the moor?"

"That I did," said the beekeeper. "And why not?"

"We're travelers," the gypsy told him. "Folks don't have no use for travelers as a rule."

"Is that a reason why a horse should be going without the dinner he's earned?" asked the lad hotly.

"'Tis more than many would do," the gypsy returned.

"Then they should feel shame for themselves!" the beekeeper told him, and he started to back his horse to get ready to turn and go homeward.

"Thank you kindly," said the gypsy lad. "I'd be glad if I——" then he broke off and asked, "What's that you have?"

The beekeeper had brought the hare along with him, tucked inside his jacket. It had popped its head out and was looking at the gypsy man.

"'Tis a hare," said the lad, bringing it out and setting it on his knee for the gypsy to see.

"There aren't any blue-eyed hares!" said the gypsy.

"Och, now, there are indeed, for you see one here before you," the beekeeper told him good-naturedly.

"Grandam!" shouted the gypsy. When a voice from inside the van answered, the gypsy called, "Come out and tell this gentleman there are no blue-eyed hares."

An old woman climbed down from the back of the van and came up to the side of the beekeeper's cart. She leaned over and looked at the hair with her old watery eyes.

" 'Tis no hare," she said, shaking her head.

"What would it be then if not a hare?" asked the bewildered beekeeper.

The old woman took the hare from his knee and felt it over gently. " 'Tis a lassie, sir!" she said, " 'Tis a lassie, and somebody's bewitched her and turned her into a hare."

"Och!" said the lad. "Then I can say who it was! 'Twas that old besom that came o'er the moor seeking to buy her from me. She was just trying to get her back again, and maybe she might have, only the bees wouldn't let her."

"Are you friends with the bees?" asked the old woman.

"I love them well," said the lad simply.

"Do you know their language?" she asked.

"Och, I can't say that I do," the beekeeper replied. "What they say when they are buzzing around is beyond me, though they do seem to understand what I say well enough."

"Well, if they understand you," said the gypsy woman, " 'twill be good enough. Now, heed what I say! The old woman will try again. She's afraid of the bees and is only waiting until she thinks they've taken to their hives for the winter. The time you have to fear most is All Hallows' Eve. That's when the witches are at the top of their power and no doubt she'll be after the hare that night."

"Tell the gentleman what he's to do, Grandam," said the gypsy man impatiently.

"Give me a bit of time," the old woman said. "I'd not like to be paying for the gentleman's kindness by telling him wrong. Go slow and go thorough. 'Tis the best way."

She turned back to the beekeeper and said, "When you get home, you must go to your bees and tell them you're in trouble and need their help. Tell them all that I have told you. If the bees are willing to help you when All Hallows' Eve comes round, leave your house door open, but get yourself and the hare away from the house and away from the moor as far as you can go. Tie the hare by the neck to your arm with a good stout cord and hold her fast in your arm, for when midnight comes, she'll try to get away from you because of the witch's spells. No matter how she twists and turns, you must hold on to her. It may go well and it may go ill for you. I can do no more for you."

She handed the hare back to the lad and climbed into the van again. The driver thanked the lad again for bringing the grain, and the lad thanked him for the help he'd got from the gypsies. Then they parted and went their separate ways.

The lad went back to his house and went from hive to hive, telling his bees what the old gypsy woman had told him, and asking them for their help on All Hallows' Eve.

He could hear a great commotion in the hives. "Bzzzzz! Bzzzzz! Bzzzzz!" said the bees, over and over again. What they were saying he didn't know at all except that they sounded uncommonly angry and upset.

When the day of All Hallows' Eve came, the beekeeper harnessed his horse to the market cart. He tied the blue-eyed hare to his arm with a good stout cord and took her on his arm. He got into the cart, turned away from the moor and took the rough road over which the gypsy van had gone. And he left the house door open wide behind him.

On and on and on he drove, through wood and past meadow and bog and glen. Day passed and twilight fell and gave away to night. But the way was clear, for the moon was bright, so the beekeeper and the blue-eyed hare went on and on and on.

Suddenly, the hare gave a spring in his arms as if it would leap from the cart. The beekeeper knew that midnight had come, so he stopped the cart and clasped the hare tight.

A cloud came over the moon and he could not see, for all was dark around him. The hare writhed and twisted and turned in his arms, and once he thought he'd lost her. But the good stout cord held fast and he got her back into his arms again, and this time she didn't get away. All at once she stopped struggling and he could feel that there was something bigger than a hare that he held in his arms. At that moment the moon shone out again and all was bright as day. What he saw in his arms was a blue-eyed lass and the bonniest he'd ever seen! There was a good stout cord around her neck and

the other end of it was tied to his arm. He took the cord from her neck and from his arm, and set her beside him.

Nobody needed to tell them that the spell had been lifted from the lass. They could see that for themselves! So he took up the reins, and away they went to find a town where they could be married.

It took them a week to get back home, for they went the long way round by the market town, instead of going back the way they had come.

As they were coming through the town, whom should they meet but the man who had told the beekeeper that the old woman was a witch. He ran up to their cart and said to the beekeeper, "Do you mind that old woman you asked me about that I told you was a witch? Och, well! They found her the morn after All Hallows' Eve lying dead out on the moor! The strange part of it is that the doctors all say she was stung to death by bees. Now how can that be, with never a bee out at this time o' the year?"

"I wouldn't know," said the beekeeper. "But strange things do happen." And he smiled down at his blue-eyed wife.

Then the beekeeper and his wife drove back across the moor, and came safe home. The first thing they did was to go out to the hives and tell the bees that they were married and to thank them for their help.

And the bees said, "Bzzz-zzz. Bzzz-zzz. Bzzz-zzz." in a sleepy satisfied way.

The Fisherlad
and the Mermaid's Ring

ONCE THERE WAS A LAD WHO OFFERED HIS HEART TO A bonny lass. She smiled at him kindly and spoke to him softly, but she would not have his heart at all, because she loved somebody else. So she told the lad that he must take his heart and find another lass to give it to.

"It will be a long long day and I shall go a long long way ere I do that!" said he. And he stomped away from her, sure that he'd never find a lass that could ever take her place.

He was a fisherman, but when she would not have him, he would go no more to the shore with the other lads, lest they put shame upon him for having misgiven his heart. So he took up his nets and sailed away, until he came to a cove where no one save himself ever came. There on the shore he built himself a hut to bide in. From the cove he sailed each day alone to set his nets and draw up his fish. The fish he caught he took to market at a port where he was a stranger, for he would not show his face again in a place where he was known.

So day in and day out he set his nets and drew up his fish and nursed his sorrow. When he had been away for a year and a day, as he drew up his nets from the sea he saw there was something strange among the fish in one of them. He thought at first that it was only a great fish, but when he had the net clear of the water he looked closer. Then he saw that it was a mermaid.

Quick as a wink he caught it by the arm through the mesh of the net and, though it struggled hard, he held it fast. He tipped the fish out, but he kept hold of the mermaid all the while. Then he wrapped the folds of the net tight about it so that it wouldn't be getting away from him. He set the creature up before him on one of the thwarts of the boat, and looked it over to see what it was like. What he saw was a lass like any other lass as far down as her waist. But from there she was like a fish, all covered with shining bright scales.

The mermaid set to weeping and begged him to let her go, but the fisherman shook his head. "Nay, I'll not do that!" he said.

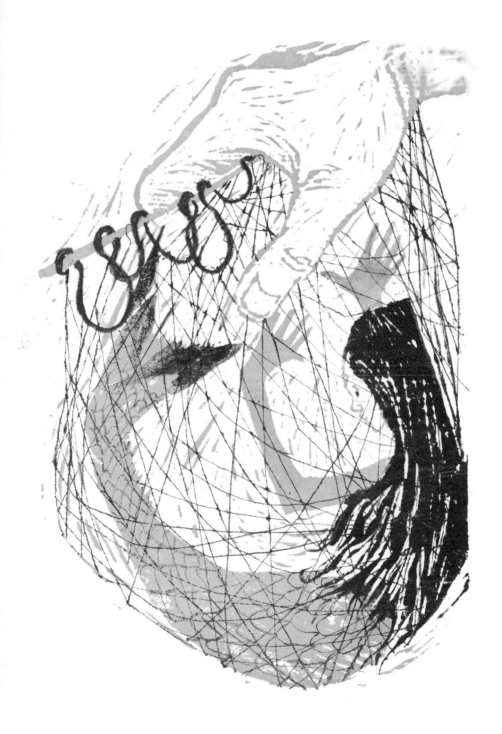

"On the floor of the sea are many great ships that have foundered in the storms," the mermaid said. "Let me go and I'll fetch you a kist of gold from one of them."

"What good is gold to me?" asked the fisherman. "'Twill not give me what I want."

"My father is one of the kings of the sea," said the mermaid. "His castle is made of the pearls of the sea and he has rich treasures of precious gems. Set me free and he will send you a ransom of gold from his store."

"What good are jewels to me? They will not give me what I want," said the lad.

"What is it that you want then?" asked the mermaid.

"I want the lass I love best in all the world," said the lad. "She's not to be had for gold nor jewels, nor will a true heart win her. For I offered her my own and she would not take it. But there's not a lass her equal in all the weary world."

"What is she like then that makes her so different?"

"She has two blue eyes," said the lad.

"So has many another lass," said the mermaid.

"But not the like of hers," said he.

The mermaid smiled. "And what more?" she asked.

"She has hair the gold of the midday sun," said the lad.

"So has many another lass," said the mermaid.

"But not the like of hers," said he.

"Eyes of blue and golden hair," said the mermaid.
122 "Well—and what more?"

"She is tall and straight and supple as a young ash tree," said the lad.

"So is many another lass," said the mermaid. "To me she does not seem greatly different. But what more?"

"Och, what does it matter?" cried the lad. "What I want above all in the world is the lass I love and if I can't have her, I want naught else!"

"The lass you love," said the mermaid thoughtfully. "I think we could give you even that, if you will but let me go free."

"Nay," said the lad. "You'll ne'er do that. I doubt that she'll be wedded by now."

"She'll not be," promised the mermaid. "But you will have to come with me to my father. He is the one who can give you what you wish. Do you dare come with me into the sea?"

"I dare!" said the lad. Hope had cast out all fear from his heart.

So he cut the net from the mermaid and she took him by the hand and drew him down under the sea to her father's castle.

The sea king sat on a throne of pearl in his great hall. He greeted his daughter with joy, for the fishes had brought him word that she had been caught in the fisherlad's net. When his daughter told him her story, he was not pleased that she should be bargained for like a catch of fish in the market. But a promise was a promise and her word was as good as his own. Besides, she was so dear to him and he was so glad to have her safe that he was ready to give the lad what he asked.

"So, you want the lass you love best in all the world?" said the sea king. "Well! 'Twill take a bit of doing to get you that. Could you bear to wait a bit longer if you got what you wanted in the end?"

It could be borne, the lad said, if it had to be.

"For another year and a day," said the sea king, "you must bide in your cove and do as you have done day in and night out. Though the time seem long and you grow weary of waiting, 'tis what you must do."

"I'll do so then!" said the lad.

Then the sea king sent for a casket of jewels, and from it he took a ring of gold all set round with pearls.

"You did well," said the king, "to refuse to take gold or jewels for my daughter's freedom, for neither of them ever gives true happiness. When the year and the day are over, if you go to the lass you love best in all the world, you'll find her waiting for you. Take this ring and keep it carefully, and when you find her, put it on her finger and wed her with it."

The lad took the ring and thanked the king for it. Then the king had a great fish carry him back to his cove. There, everything was just as he left it except that his boat was drawn up on the shore. The sails were furled and the nets within it were mended where he had cut them. The sea king had taken care of all that, too.

The lad went up to his hut and laid off his wet clothes to dry. The ring he laid on the chimney shelf against the time when he'd be needing it.

So he started out to serve his time, setting his nets and drawing up his fish and taking them to be sold. It was not sorrow that he nursed now, but hope for the day when he'd be claiming his own true love.

No more than a week had gone by when he came home one night in the gloaming, and as he drew his boat up out of the sea, he saw what he took to be a heap of seaweed lying upon the stone of his doorstep. He wondered how it came to be there, and hurried up from the shore to see.

When he got there, he found that it was not seaweed, but a lass who crouched on the doorstone. Her face was hidden in her lap and her hair streamed down around her. It was her hair that he had taken for seaweed because it was brown and so thick and long that it covered her to the ground.

When she heard his footstep, she sat up and her hair fell away from her face. Then he saw that her face was wet and her eyes were red with weeping. He was in no mood for anybody's troubles but his own, so he asked her roughly, "What are you doing here?"

"I've run off from my father's house," she told him.   125

"There's a new stepmother there and she no older than my-self. There's no place for me there because she can't abide me, and I came away lest she do me some harm."

"Then you'd best run back again," said the lad. "For there's no place for you here, either."

"Och, do not drive me away," begged the lass. "I've wandered many a weary mile and found no place where they'd take me in. Let me stay, and I'll keep your house and cook your food and do for you all I can."

"I can do for myself," said the lad.

At that the lass burst into tears again. "I can go no farther," she wept in despair. "If I cannot bide here, I must just go down and jump into the sea!"

The lad could no longer bear the sight and sound of her grief. His heart filled with pity for her and he said more gently, "Whisht, lass! Bide here then, if you like. Only keep out of my way."

So she stayed. True to her word, she kept the house and kept it as bright and shining as a new pin—what there was of it. And as he had commanded, she kept out of his way. The only times he saw her at all were when she served him his meals. She kept herself back in a corner even then, and came forward only to fill his plate again or give him something he was looking about for. When she ate or where she stayed for the rest of the time, he never thought to ask.

So it went on for a week or two, with him at his fishing

and her at her housework, and he saw and heard so little of her 'twas as if she wasn't there.

Then, one night as he was coming up from his boat, he thought it was a foolish sort of thing for two human souls to bide in one house and hold so little converse together. So he went in and he said, "Set yourself a place on the table across from me, lass, and eat your supper like a Christian!" and so she did.

After they had sat together at meals for a week or two, they began to find words to say to each other. Soon they knew all there was to know about each other. He said that she'd done well to leave her father's house, and she said the blue eyes and golden hair and the grace of his true love must be the wonder of the world! So, since they were so well agreed, both of them were content.

About that time, she took to coming down to the shore of an evening to help him beach the boat and spread the nets. She was only a wee thing, and it gave him a laugh to see her lay hold of the big boat. But for all that, she was sturdy, so her help was worth something to him. He was glad enough to have it when he came in tired after the day's work.

It came to his mind once, as she ran up the path before him to make sure his supper'd be good and hot, that she was bonny enough in her own way. To be sure, there was naught of the blue and gold of his true love about her and she'd never be reminding a man of a young ash tree. She was as brown of skin and hair and eye as an autumn hazelnut, and so small you'd be taking her for a bairn at first sight. But for all that, she was neatly made, and she was as light on her feet as a dry leaf borne on the wind.

Before he knew it, half of the days of his time were over. She was the one who told him so, for she had figured it out on a chart she'd made, marking the days off one by one. It was right clever of her, he said, for he'd have never thought of doing such a thing himself.

Now that they were so well acquainted, she began to grow bolder. She never could be happy unless she was busying herself with something or other. It wasn't enough that the house was tidy and clean. First, it was flowers that she brought from the fields to plant by the house wall. Then it was a wild rose that she trained to twine above the door. Now, she began to ask him to fetch things from the town where he sold his fish. He must bring glass for the window holes to keep the weather out. He grumbled a bit, but he brought the glass and made frames for it too, and fitted the windows into their places in the wall.

Then she said the room was too bare, so he must fetch her a bit of goods for her to be making curtains of. He told her they'd been getting along well enough before they ever had either glass or curtains for the windows. But she only said that that was then and this was now, and for him to be off because she had work to do even if he didn't.

Then he must bring some white to wash the walls with inside, for the room was too dreary and dark. What with one thing and another, he complained that she wore him out and kept his pocket light.

It was about this time that he found out that she'd been laying a pallet in the shed to sleep on of nights among the oars and the fishing gear. He'd never given a thought to where she slept, but when he found it out, he took steps to change it. He laid off from his fishing for a time and got busy at it.

When she saw him about the place, measuring and hauling stone and hacking at this and that, she came out to watch him. "What will you be at now?" she asked.

"I'm building a room to the house," said he.

"Whatever for?" said she.

"For you to have a place for yourself," he told her. "'Tisn't seemly that you should be sleeping amongst the bait and the boat gear."

"Och!" said she and went back into the house. But he heard her singing as she went about her work, and it came to his mind that his mother used to do the same.

So the days slipped by. Soon there were a wheen of them marked off on the lass's chart and but a few days left to be marked.

The house had a but and a ben with glass in the windows of both of the rooms and curtains to all of the windows, as well as glass. The walls were white as milk, and there was a drugget on the floor that the lass had made herself, and a hearth with a hob that the lad had built. There was a fire on the hearth and a shining kettle singing on the hob. And on the shelf above the fire was a clock that the lad had brought from the town, ticking busily beside the sea king's pearl ring.

One day the lad came in and caught the lass with the ring upon her finger. She was holding up her hand and looking at the ring.

"What are you doing there!" he asked sharply.

She jumped and looked frighted. "Och!" said she. "I was just having a look at it!"

"Well, put it away and do not do so again!" he ordered, going on out to the shed to put his gear away.

"Till you give me leave," she said softly to his back. But he didn't hear her. She slipped the ring from her finger and laid it back in its place on the shelf by the clock.

When he came back she said to him, "I'll soon be leaving here."

"You will!" said he. "Why will you then?"

"The year and the day will soon be up and you'll be going to fetch your own true love," she told him.

"You'd best stay here," said the lad.

"Och, I'd not be liking to do that," she said.

"Where can you go then?" he asked her.

"Back to my father's house," said she.

"Are you not afraid to go back there?" he asked.

"Nay! I'm a lot older now," said she. "I can look after myself."

"A lot older!" he scoffed. " 'Tis but a year that's gone by and hardly that!"

"Happen I'm a lot wiser then," said the lass. "I'll go there anyway."

So he said no more about it nor did she.

But a few days later she rose at day's dawning and made herself a packet of all she had of her own in the world. There was little enough to take. Just her comb and an apron or two she'd made for herself, a knot of ribbon and a kerchief he'd brought her from the town, and her nightshift. When she'd packed them all, she took the bundle under her arm and laid her shawl over her shoulders. Then she went out to the lad. She took the chart from the shelf behind the clock and laid it before him where he sat at the table. And she marked the last days off.

"All of the days of your waiting are over today," said she. "You'll be going to claim your own true love tomorrow. So I'll wish you well and bid you farewell!"

Then she walked past him and out of the house.

He sat there for a long while staring at the door through which she had gone, like a man who has heard something but not believed his ears. When he jumped up at last and went to the door to look after her, she was out of sight.

The lad went back and sat down again in the place where 131

he'd been sitting when she went away. All that day he did not go out in his boat nor move from his chair. He thought over all the days that had gone by since the day he caught the mermaid in his net. It took him all the hours of the day to do it. When he was through, he went to bed.

The next morning he got up at break of dawn and dressed himself in the best he had. He took the sea king's ring from the shelf and tucked it into his pocket, and started off to claim his own true love.

But it wasn't down to his boat he went, to sail back home. Instead, he turned away from the sea, and walked inland the same way the lass had gone the day before.

She was walking in her father's garden when she saw him coming up the road. When he got up to her and spoke to her, she turned red and white by turns. But she spoke right up to him.

"I thought you had gone to claim your own true love," said she.

"I have so!" said he. "That's what I'm doing here!" And he took the sea king's ring from his pocket and held it out to her.

"Will you have it?" he asked her. "And me with it, of course!"

"If you give me leave!" said she. And she took the ring from his hand and slipped it on her finger.

So they were wed and a grand time it was to be sure! Every-

one danced until they could dance no more. Then when they'd rested a while they started in all over again. Even the new young stepmother danced at the lass's wedding and was glad to do it, for the two of them had made it up and were good friends in the end.

When it was all over, the lad took the lass back to his own village. He was that proud of her that he wanted them to have a look at her. Whom should he meet there but his old love! Her eyes were as blue and her hair was as gold, and she was as straight and tall and slim as ever. But she didn't look any different to him now from a lot of other blue-eyed, yellow-haired lasses he'd met in his life.

Then he tucked his wee brown bride under his arm, and took her back to the house on the shore of the cove, which was where both of them wanted to be.

The eve of the day they got there they walked down to the shore, and who should they find there sitting on a rock out in the water but the mermaid.

"Did you get your own true love?" the mermaid asked of the lad.

"I did so!" said the lad. "And here she is!"

The mermaid took a look at the lass. "Her eyes are not blue," said she.

"They are not," the lad agreed.

"And she has not golden hair," the mermaid said.

"She has not," said the lad.

"And I should call her neither slim nor tall," the mermaid said.

"Nay. She's a wee thing and perhaps a bit on the plump side," said the lad. "But she is the one I love the best of all."

"Well then," said the mermaid, "you'll not be saying we did not give you what you asked for." And at that she divit off the rock and into the sea, and that was the last they ever saw of her.

But they never forgot her. Because they knew it was from her and her father, the sea king, that the lad had got his own true love and all the happiness that came with her.

Michael Scott
and the Demon

THERE WAS A MAN AND HIS NAME WAS MICHAEL SCOTT and he was a wizard. He had the knowledge on him of black magic and white magic and the whole of the shades between and he was a great man entirely.

This same Michael Scott it was who stopped the plague, when it got to Scotland, by gathering the lot of it up into his bag and shutting it tight within. As the plague was the De'il's own work, he put the bag where the De'il would not be getting at it to let it loose again. And that was in a vault

at Glenluce Abbey in Galloway where the De'il would not

be liking to go, it being too holy a place for the likes of him.

That put the De'il against Michael Scott, so he sent one of his demons to be troubling him at his work.

It was just the sort of a job for the demon, he being young and full of mischief. So Michael Scott had a terrible time of it after the demon came. What with his pots being o'erturned, his cauldon boiling over, his fire smoking, and one thing and another, he'd have had less time wasted if he had just sat with his hands folded.

It was beyond bearing! So Michael Scott set his mind to mend matters, so that he could go on with his magic arts in peace.

First, he tried to catch the demon, but that one was too nimble and couldn't be caught. Then he tried to set a spell on him, but spells only seemed to make the demon livelier. So at last Michael Scott had the idea of trying to make a bargain with him.

One day, when the demon was hopping around doing whatever mischief he could, Michael Scott said to him, "Och, now, 'tis weary work this must be for you what with all the flitting around you've got to do. Sit ye down and rest yourself for a while and let's have a gab together."

"Och, I'm not weary at all," the demon said. "It suits me fine to be busy." But being willing to oblige Michael, he perched himself on the edge of the hob, anyway.

"I can see that fine," said Michael Scott. "But can you not go and be busy elsewhere?"

"That I cannot," said the demon, "because my master has sent me to attend to you."

" 'Tis sad," said Michael Scott. "Such a wearying job for a braw young lad like yourself. Is there no way you could be getting out of it?"

"There is not," said the demon cheerfully. "But it suits me fine, anyway."

"Och, aye," said Michael Scott. "But that is for now whilst it's all new to you. However, I'm none so old and 'tis likely I'll live long. The heart of me aches to think of the long weary years you have ahead of you. It does indeed!"

The demon stopped looking so cheerful. "That may be so," said he, "but nevertheless I must just make the best of it."

"Aye," sighed Michael Scott. "So you must. And there's no way at all that you could be rid of the job?"

"None," said the demon, sighing, too, in spite of himself. "Barring one."

"And what would that one be?" Michael asked kindly, taking care not to seem too interested and eager.

"Well, if you could be setting me a task that was too much for me so I'd not be able to do it," the demon told him. Then he laughed, and added, "Never fear! That you ne'er could do."

"Well, 'tis worth trying," said Michael Scott. "We could make sort of a game of it. 'Twould be a change for us both and make time pass quicker."

Well, the demon could see the sense of that. He'd been overturning pots and smothering fires and the like for a fortnight past. It was a bit monotonous, if you came to look at it straight. And it could get more so as years went by. He would like a change himself for a bit of diversion.

"Give us a task then!" he said with a chuckle, being terribly sure of himself.

Michael Scott thought for a minute or two. Then he said, "River Tweed does need a cauld to it up by Kelso Town. No man's ever been able to build one, for the water there runs too fast and deep. Would you like to be taking that in hand?"

"I will so!" said the demon, and off he went.

Michael Scott had one night to work in peace, but no more than that. The next morn, in came the demon very full of himself with his chest stuck out and a grin on his face that stretched from ear to ear.

" 'Tis done!" said he, putting a foot on the fire to set it smoking, and o'erturning a pot or two.

"Is it now?" said Michael Scott, hiding his disappointment as well as he could. "Och! 'Tis something harder I should have asked you to do, for I'd have been able to do that myself."

"Have another try!" said the demon, laughing at him.

"That I will," said Michael Scott. "You'll be knowing Ercildoune Hill where it sets in the plain like a big sugar loaf? Well then! Break it up and make three hills of it, if you can."

"I'll be at it at once!" the demon said. "I'll be finding it easier far than last night's work."

So Michael Scott had another night's peace. He did no work in it but he set his wits to work for him. He sat in his chair and thought and thought and thought. He misdoubted that the demon would be back on the morrow's morn, and he wanted to be ready with a task that would free him from the demon for good and all.

Well, back the demon came the next morning, and the grin on his face was wide enough to near split his head in two. " 'Twas no trouble at all," he told Michael Scott gleefully. "I'd have been back long ere this, did I not stop to hear the commotion of the people to see three hills this morn where only one was the night before. 'Tis sore befuddled and

bemazed they are, to be sure!'' And he screeched with laughter at the memory.

"I'm hoping you'll have something as easy and entertaining for me to do next," he told Michael Scott.

"Och," said Michael Scott, putting on a doleful air. "I fear you are too much for me. 'Tis past believing the wonders you can bring about. I'm just at the point of giving it all up."

"Och, come now," said the demon kindly. "Give it another try, anyway." He looked pleased at the praise Michael had given him.

"Happen 'tis too trifling a task for a lad with powers like your own," Michael Scott said reluctantly.

"Nay! Nay!" said the demon. "Tell me then. I'll not be offended."

"Well then," said Michael hesitating-like, " 'Tis not much, but I'd like it fine if you'd go down by the sea and make me a few fathom of rope from the sand on the shore there."

"I will so!" cried the demon happily. "And be back in time for my tea. 'Tis the softest task of them all!"

So off he went and left Michael Scott with a promise that he'd not be long gone.

But he never came back again. For Michael's last bidding had stumped him entirely. To this very day the demon is still there by the sea trying to make ropes of sand, and all in vain.

When the wind blows high and the waves beat the shore, if you listen you'll hear him whispering, "R-r-r-r-ropes of s-s-s-s-sand! R-r-r-r-ropes of s-s-s-s-sand!" as he works away at the task he ne'er can do.

So Michael Scott had peace at his magic for all the rest of his days. Even the De'il himself did not bother him any more, for he was afraid if he did, Michael Scott would get the best of him, too.